Science is about asking questions. Chemistry is the science that asks questions about the chemical world around you, its practical uses, and some of the social issues it raises.

You will find this book useful if you are studying chemistry as part of the AQA Modular Science Single or Double Award GCSE science course.

Everything in this book has been organized to help you find out things quickly and easily. It is written in two-page units called spreads.

Use the contents page

If you are looking for information on a large topic, look it up in the contents page.

Use the index

If there is something small you want to check on, look up the most likely word in the index. The index gives the page number where you'll find information about that word.

Use the questions

Asking questions and answering them is a very good way of learning. There are questions at the end of every Module. At the end of the book there is a set of further exam-style questions and a selection of multiple-choice questions. Answers to numerical questions, and some pointers to those requiring short answers, are provided.

Use the key words glossary

At the end of each Module there are a selection of key words and their meanings to help you understand the main ideas given in the Module.

Helping you revise

To help you revise, in addition to the questions and the end-of-Module glossaries of important terms, there are some revision notes and some further exam-style questions.

Chemistry is an important and exciting subject. It doesn't just happen in laboratories. It is all around you: in fairgrounds, fields, farms, and factories. It is taking place deep in the Earth and far out in space. You'll find chemistry everywhere.

I hope that this book helps you with your studies, that you enjoy using it, and that at the end of your course, you agree with me!

Pat O'Brien
July 2001

Notes:
- *the real world 'application spreads' may contain materials outside the AQA specification.*
- *Appendix A3 contains additional statutory material for the national curriculum in Northern Ireland*

Chemistry Contents

Written for the NEW **AQA** Specification

Target Science

Chemistry
Foundation Tier

AQA Modular Science

Pat O'Brien

OXFORD
UNIVERSITY PRESS

OXFORD
UNIVERSITY PRESS

Great Clarendon Street, Oxford OX2 6DP

Oxford University Press is a department of the University of Oxford.
It furthers the University's objective of excellence in research, scholarship,
and education by publishing worldwide in

Oxford New York

Athens Auckland Bangkok Bogotá Buenos Aires Cape Town
Chennai Dar es Salaam Delhi Florence Hong Kong Istanbul Karachi
Kolkata Kuala Lumpur Madrid Melbourne Mexico City Mumbai Nairobi
Paris São Paulo Shanghai Singapore Taipei Tokyo Toronto Warsaw
with associated companies in Berlin Ibadan

Oxford is a registered trade mark of Oxford University Press
in the UK and in certain other countries

British Library Cataloguing in Publication Data

Data available

ISBN 0-19-914837-6

Typeset in Stone Serif
by Ian Foulis & Associates, Plymouth UK
Printed in Spain by Gráficas Estella

Acknowledgements

The publisher would like to thank the following for their kind permission to reproduce copyright material:

Cover Stone; pp8/9 Corbis/S Raymer; p12 Still from BBC Open University video 'The Elements Organized in the Periodic Table' (top), Corbis (bottom); p14 Austin J Brown
(top left), Still Pictures/R Giling (top right), Ancient Art & Architecture Collection/R Sheridan (bottom left), Ancient Art & Architecture Collection/S Coyne (bottom centre),
Ancient Art & Architecture Collection/R Sheridan (bottom right); p15 SPL/Rosenfeld Images; p16 Andrew Lambert (all); p18 Andrew Lambert (all); p19 Natural History
Museum (top left, centre and right), Andrew Lambert (bottom); p20 Corbis (top), Andrew Lambert (bottom); p21 Andrew Lambert; p22 GSF (top, centre left, and centre),
Natural History Museum (centre right), Andrew Lambert (bottom left and centre), Science Museum/Science & Society Picture Library; p23 GSF (all); p25 SPL/Rosenfeld
Images (left), Collections/L Stares (centre), Anthony Blake/G Kirk (right); p28 Andrew Lambert (top left, centre and right); p29 Alcan Aluminium; p30 John Frost; p31
Andrew Lambert (all); p36 Environmental Images/V Miles; p40 Barnaby's Picture Library; p42 Bridgeman Art Library (top), Medipics (upper left), Mary Evans Picture
Library (centre), Redferns/Hutson (upper right), Andrew Lambert (lower left and right); p43 OUP; pp48/49 Corel Professional Pictures; p50 GSF (left and two insets),
London Arial Photo Library (centre and right); p51 GSF (top), Collections/J Miller (bottom); p52 from top to bottom Corbis, Corbis, Britstock-IFA/Geodel, Corbis, Corbis,
Corbis, James Davis, Corbis; p53 Colorsport (top), Proctor and Gamble (centre), John Birdsall (bottom); p54 John Frost (left), GSF (right); p55 Ann Ronan Picture Library;
p56 Barnaby's Picture Library/D Styles (left), Barnaby's Picture Library/S Ellis (right); p57 Environmental Images/R Roberts; p60 Andrew Lambert; p62 Neste Chemicals
(top left), Corbis (top right), Collections/G Wright (bottom right); p63 Panasonic (top), Corbis (bottom left and right); p64 Associated Press (top), Ecoscene/I Harwood
(bottom); p65 Ecoscene/S Morgan; p66 NASA; p78 Andrew Lambert (all); p79 Andrew Lambert (top left, upper left and lower left), GSF (bottom left, top right, upper right
and lower right); p80 John Birdsall (top), GSF/W Higgs (bottom); p81 GSF (all); p82 GSF(all); p83 GSF (left), Collections/D Burrows (right); p84 Tropix (top left), John Birdsall
(top right), GSF (bottom centre left, centre right, and right); p85 GSF (top left), Bridgeman Art Library (bottom left and right); p87 GSF (all); pp92/93 Corel Professional
Pictures; p94 Allsport UK/A Steele (left), Al Messerschmidt (right); p96 GSF (left), Still Pictures/Vilarino-Unep (centre), SPL/Crown Copyright (right); p99 Andrew Lambert
(all); p102 CEPHAS/M Rock (left), Andrew Lambert (right); p104 SPL; p105 Nigel Blyth (top), Andrew Lambert (bottom); p108 Thermite Welding GB; p109 Still Pictures/J B
Pierme, Andrew Lambert (centre left and right), Professional Sport (right); p111 Andrew Lambert (all); p112 John Birdsall; p114 Holt Studios/N Cattlin (left), Holt
Studios/B Ullbagen (top right), Ecoscene/F p116 BOC Gases; p115 Ecoscene/A Jones; p118 Holt Studios/N Cattlin (top left), Still Pictures/M Edwards (top right), Still
Pictures/M Edwards; p121 Agco; Blackburn (bottom left and right); p122 Andrew Lambert; pp130/131 Corbis/D G Houser; p132 Digital Vision (top and bottom), Anglo-
Australian Observatory/Royal Observatory Edinburgh; p133 NASA/J Hester and P Scowen (top left), NASA/W Brandner, E K Grebel, and You-Hua Chu (top right), European
Southern Observatory (centre left), Digital Vision (centre right and bottom right), NASA/J Klemaszewski, T A Rector, B Wolpa, M Hanna (bottom left); p134 Peter Gould;
p138 Derby Museum and Art Gallery; p139 Corbis; p146 SPL/P Plailly; p161 Ardea/S Hopkin (left), SPL/NASA (top centre and right), Ardea (bottom right); p162 NASA;
p173 SPL/S Fraser (top left), Britstock-IFA/Southern Stock (top right), SPL/A Bartel (centre left), Britstock-IFA (centre right), Ace/R Allen (bottom left), SPL/A Tsiaras (bottom
right); p174 Science Museum; p176 Mary Evans Picture Library; p177 Corel Professional Photos (all); p178 Andrew Lambert (all)

The illustrations are by Ian Foulis & Associates, J. Haslam, C. Goodyer, R. Walker

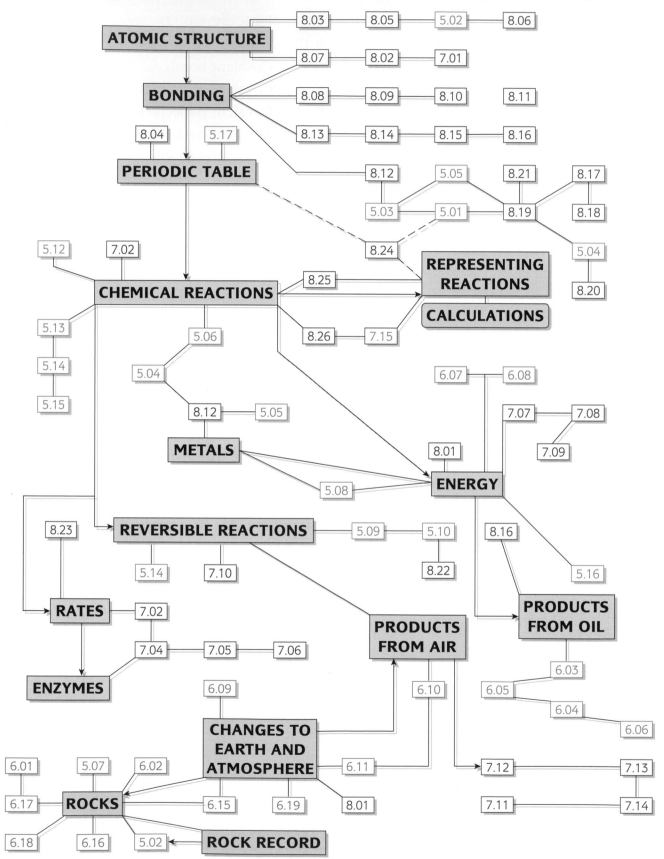

Although you will probably work through the AQA Specification Module by Module, these *Routemaps* offer alternative pathways through topics. They are particularly useful when revising as they help you identify and revise small sections at a time. They are also helpful to use to catch up if for any reason you have missed any work.

Metals

Module 5

Humans have mined metal ores for centuries. We use these materials in furnaces to produce the metals you are familiar with. Pure metals and those specially mixed with other metals or materials have made a great impact on life on this planet.

Elements and the periodic table

Elements

The Greeks had used the word 'element' to describe the building blocks of nature. Robert Boyle (1627–1691) gave us the first modern idea of chemical elements. Today we define an element as:

> a substance made of only one kind of atom.

Developing the periodic table

Dmitri Mendeleev (1834–1907) was an expert card player, especially at patience. Playing cards means being good at spotting patterns and using them to win a game. On a train journey Mendeleev wrote out the properties of the elements on cards and played a kind of patience to find the pattern which led to the **periodic table**.

By 1869, when Mendeleev drew up his first periodic table, the list of known elements had grown to 63.

Mendeleev's original periodic table.

Did you know?

John Newlands (1837–1898) found that if he arranged the elements according to increasing atomic weight, every eighth element had similar chemical and physical properties. He felt this was like a musical scale, where every eighth note is the same but at a higher or lower pitch so he suggested that the elements obeyed a periodic 'law of octaves'.

This shows how Mendeleev arranged his elements. How did he do it? He used the atomic weight, which we now call relative atomic mass. The mass of an atom is compared with that of a standard atom. Today we use carbon-12 as the standard. The mass of a hydrogen atom is $\frac{1}{12}$ the mass of a carbon atom. So its relative atomic mass is 1. Mendeleev left gaps for elements not yet discovered. He knew they would be found eventually.

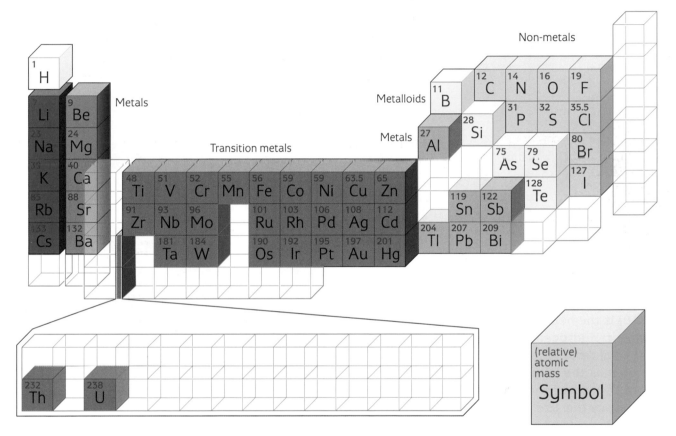

Part of the modern periodic table showing some of Mendeleev's elements. The atomic weights (relative atomic masses) have been corrected to more recent values. You can see the gaps for elements 'unknown' to Mendeleev. Vertical columns in the periodic table are known as groups. Elements in groups have similar properties.

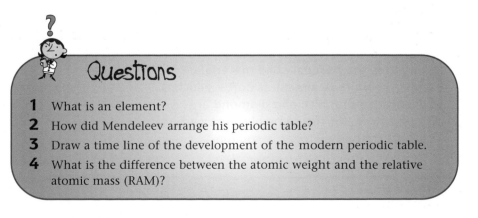

Questions

1 What is an element?

2 How did Mendeleev arrange his periodic table?

3 Draw a time line of the development of the modern periodic table.

4 What is the difference between the atomic weight and the relative atomic mass (RAM)?

HEAVIEST - *lightest* - BIGGEST - *smallest*

uranium

hydrogen

caesium

hydrogen

HEAVY   light   **BIGGEST**   smallest

The heaviest atom is not necessarily the biggest one. The mass of an atom depends on the number of protons and neutrons in its nucleus. Uranium (relative atomic mass 238.0) is the heaviest naturally occurring element. Hydrogen (relative atomic mass 1.0) is the lightest – and also the smallest. Caesium is the biggest naturally occurring atom. It has half the mass of uranium but is over twice the size!

Caesium and water react explosively!

HARDEST – softest

Diamond is the hardest solid material in nature. Graphite is almost as soft – which is odd, because graphite and diamond are different forms of the same element: carbon! The softest solid element is sodium.

The  longest bonds in nature – a tale of murder

Bonds between atoms are not still. They vibrate. They bend. They twist. How much they can do this depends upon the length and strength of the bond. The longer the bond, generally the weaker the bond.

In nature probably the longest bond is that of thallium in thallium crystals. Thallium is an element with an infamous past. In both Agatha Christie's novel *The Pale Horse* and Ngaio Marsh's thriller *Final Curtain*, thallium was used as a poison. In real life it was used as a poison in 1992. Some countries' security forces have used it to kill opponents of the government.

The body mistakes thallium for potassium, but the thallium messes up reactions in the cells. It is not all bad, however: the long bond does help to give thallium a use in making glass for highly refractive lenses and as an insecticide and rodent killer.

Metals: best conductor of electricity

The best conductor of electricity is silver, followed by copper, gold, and aluminium. Manganese is the worst metallic conductor.

Atoms of a good conductor of electricity and heat.

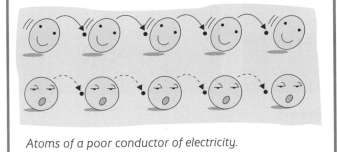

Atoms of a poor conductor of electricity.

Best and worst conductor of heat

The best non-metal conductor of heat is diamond; the worst is xenon. The best metal conductors of heat are silver, copper, gold, and aluminium; the worst is manganese.

Talking point

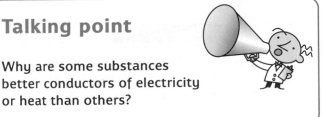

Why are some substances better conductors of electricity or heat than others?

Metals (versus non-metals)

Metal or non-metal ?

Imagine a world without either. Both metal and non-metal elements are special in their own ways. Metals have useful properties, such as conducting electricity and heat; they are strong, able to be shaped, and make a noise when struck. Non-metals, however are the basis for life.

In the periodic table over 80 of the elements are metals and 20 are non-metals. They are mainly found in the left-hand columns (Groups 1 and 2) and in the central block of transition metals.

People and metals

Since the Bronze Age, for about 4000 years, people have been extracting metals. They have melted these metals to make tools and weapons. They have either used them pure, as in iron, or mixed them to make an alloy. Copper and tin make the alloy bronze.

Steel being hot-rolled.

Did you know?

Mercury is a strange substance. It is a very dense liquid metal. In the past it was used to treat venereal disease.
It also made people mad and killed them. Charles II was killed by mercury poisoning. Isaac Newton suffered from insanity during 1692-93. This was probably because he boiled mercury in some of his experiments.

Properties of metals	Properties of non-metals
• Metals can be shaped by hammering them. They are **malleable**. This is often better done when the metal is hot. Because metals have high melting points they can be heated to very high temperatures without melting.	• Most non-metals are not strong.
	• Non-metals are not malleable
• Metals can be shaped by pulling them into thin wires. They are **ductile**.	• Non-metals are not ductile. In fact, when solid they are brittle. They are not sonorous.
	• Many are gases.
• Metals can be used to carry electricity from one place to another. They are good conductors.	• Most non-metals have low melting and boiling points.
• Metal atoms slide over each other.	• Non-metals, except graphite, are poor conductors of electricity.
• Many metals are very dense and feel heavy because their atoms are regular and closely packed.	• Non-metals can gain electrons to form ionic bonds with metals.
• Metal atoms have few electrons in their outside shell. This means they can easily lose electrons to form ionic bonds with non-metals.	• Non-metals are generally poor conductors of heat.
• Metals are shiny when polished.	
• Metals often go dull in air because they react with oxygen. This is called **corrosion**.	
• Metals are good conductors of heat.	

Some elements such as silicon and arsenic, have properties of both metals and non-metals. They are often called semi–metals or metalloids.

Non-metals

Non–metals include carbon, oxygen, sulphur, chlorine, hydrogen, and nitrogen.

Questions

1 List five properties of metals.
2 A metal is described as malleable and ductile.
   What does malleable mean? What does ductile mean?
3 List five properties of non-metals.
4 Why is graphite not a typical non-metal?

5.04 Group 1: the alkali metals

Objectives

This spread should help you to

- describe the atomic structure of the elements in Group 1 using the periodic table
- know the common reactions and physical properties of Group 1
- describe what happens to the reactivity of metals as you go down the group.

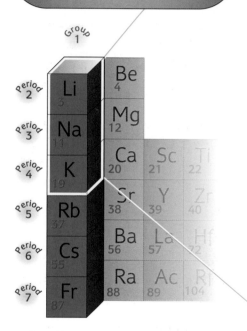

Atoms and ions

The elements in Group 1 are all metals.

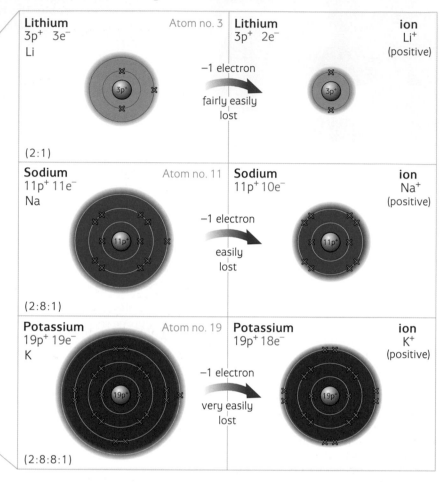

The atoms get bigger as you go down the group. They all have one electron in the outer electron shell. Group 1 metals can easily lose the electron from the outer shell and that is why they are so reactive.

Group 1 metals have such a low density that lithium, sodium, and potassium float on water. When they come into contact with water they react vigorously. They generally form colourless solutions.

Lithium reacts with water, fizzing and releasing hydrogen.

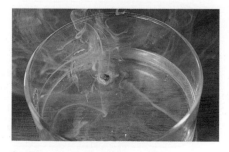

Sodium is more reactive – there is even a yellow flame.

Potassium is more reactive than sodium or lithium.

They fizz and potassium burns with a lilac flame. The fizzing is the release of hydrogen as water reacts. The metal forms a hydroxide. This dissolves in the water, so you will not see it.

Group 1 metal + water → metal hydroxide + hydrogen gas
(dissolved)

The metal hydroxide is called an **alkali**. Dissolved in water they give alkaline solutions. Group 1 metals are known as the **alkali metals**.

Physical properties

Metal	Melting Point	Boiling Point	Hardness
lithium	180 °C	1340 °C	soft
sodium	98 °C	880 °C	very soft
potassium	63 °C	760 °C	very, very soft

The melting point gets lower as you go down Group 1. This is because the attraction between the atoms gets weaker as the atoms of the metals get bigger. This also makes the metal soft: they can be cut with a knife.

Reaction with non-metals

The alkali metals form ionic compounds with non-metals. Chlorine is a green poisonous gas. If pieces of the Group 1 metals are cut and placed in chlorine they will burn. Lithium burns the slowest and potassium burns the fastest.

The Group 1 metal becomes a positive ion. Chlorine gains an electron and becomes a negative chloride ion.

The positive metal ion joins up with the negative chloride ions to make an ionic bond. The product is a **chloride**.

lithium + chlorine	→	lithium chloride
sodium + chlorine	→	sodium chloride
potassium + chlorine	→	potassium chloride

Did you know?

Modern motor cars use a sodium salt to inflate the safety airbag. Sodium azide (NaN_3) is toxic but when heated it will explode and release nitrogen gas. Air bags were first introduced in the 1980s.

Questions

1 Which group is made up of the alkali metals?

2 What is the reaction of alkali metals with water and how does it change as you go down the group?

3 Draw a graph of the change in melting and boiling points of the alkali metals. What happens to the melting or boiling points as you go down the group?

A colourful block: transition metals

Objectives

This spread should help you to

- know which block in the Periodic Table is known as the transition metals
- name the common transition metals
- describe some of their properties

Locating the transition metals

The large block of elements in the centre of the periodic table are the **transition metals**. Some of the better known are chromium, iron, cobalt, nickel, copper, zinc, silver, tungsten, and gold.

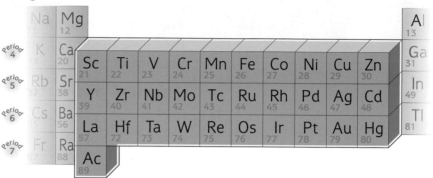

Physical properties of the transition metals

Transition metals are often referred to as typical metals. This is because they are:

- shiny
- hard
- dense
- good conductors of electricity and heat
- malleable
- ductile

Transition metals are widely used for many purposes in industry, in our homes, and around us. Compared to alkali metals they have high melting points (except mercury - a liquid).

Slow reaction with oxygen.

Reactions of the transition metals

Copper is a typical transition metal. When heated, it reacts very slowly with the oxygen in the air. When placed in water for a week it does not react with the water. Copper weather vanes will go green over time. Some transition metals will corrode when left in moist air. This is what happens to iron when it rusts.

No reaction with water.

Creating colours

Manganese(II) chloride

Iron(III) chloride

Cobalt(II) chloride

Nickel(II) chloride

Copper(II) chloride

Many transition metals form coloured salts. These salts give pottery glazes and many gemstones their colour. The green colours of these gems are caused by different transition metals:

Turquoise contains copper.

Emerald contains chromium.

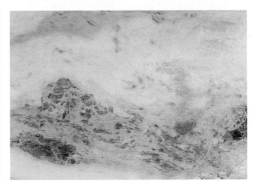

Jade contains iron.

Multiple compounds

Transition metals can often form more than one compound with the same element. For example, copper can form copper(II) oxide (CuO) or copper(I) oxide (Cu$_2$O). If the copper atom only loses one electron it will form copper(I) oxide which is red in colour. If the copper atom loses two electrons it will form copper(II) oxide which is black in colour.

Red copper(I) oxide   Black copper(II) oxide

Other uses

Transition metals can speed up reactions. When they do this they do not change chemically. They are acting as a **catalyst**. The properties of transition elements make them very useful: iron for making things strong, copper for electric cables, titanium as an alloy for making aircraft.

Questions

1 Where in the Periodic Table are the transition metals?

2 Are they metals or non-metals. Why do you think that?

3 What is different about some of their compounds compared to the compounds of ordinary metals?

4 What happens to some rocks when there is a transition metal present?

Objectives

This spread should help you to

- describe reactivity
- know the reactivity series of metals
- describe what happens when a more reactive element reacts with a compound of a less reactive element.

Reactivity

Reactivity is an important idea in chemistry. If an element *displaces* another element from a compound in a reaction, it is said to be more **reactive** than that element.

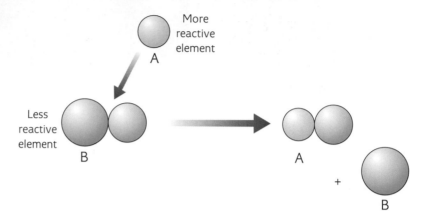

A is more reactive than B so it displaces B from the compound.

Magnesium flares burn well under water!

Magnesium is used to make alloys for aircraft. In the factory they have dry powder fire extinguishers to put out any fire. If you pour water on burning magnesium, the magnesium displaces hydrogen from the water. Hydrogen is an explosive gas and so an explosion would happen.

magnesium metal + water →
magnesium oxide + hydrogen gas

If you use a carbon dioxide extinguisher, the magnesium displaces carbon from the carbon dioxide. It combines with the oxygen: in other words, the magnesium burns even faster!

magnesium metal + carbon dioxide →
magnesium oxide + carbon

But the dry powder covers the magnesium and keeps out oxygen. The fire goes out.

The reactivity of magnesium, carbon, and oxygen could be shown like this:

Mg
O   ↑ more
C   reactive

The *reactivity series*

The **reactivity series** is a list of metals in order of their reactivity. The order mirrors the history of metals and their discovery.

Copper metal reacts with aqueous silver ions to produce silver - its nickname is the Christmas Tree reaction!

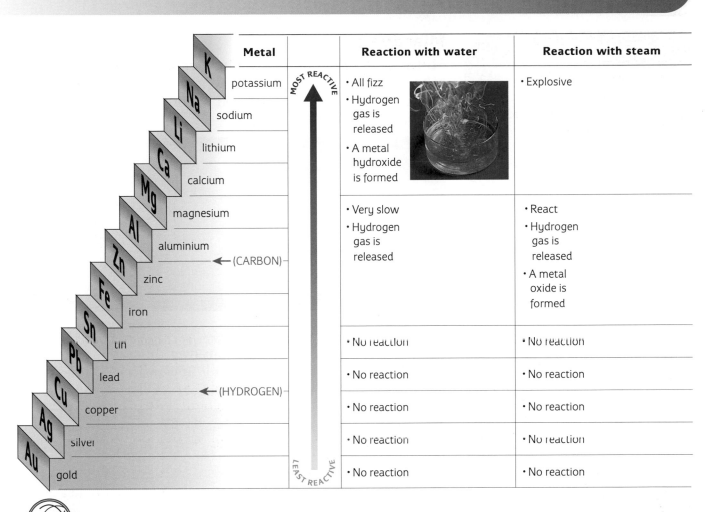

Metal		Reaction with water	Reaction with steam
K potassium	MOST REACTIVE ↑	• All fizz • Hydrogen gas is released • A metal hydroxide is formed	• Explosive
Na sodium			
Li lithium			
Ca calcium			
Mg magnesium		• Very slow • Hydrogen gas is released	• React • Hydrogen gas is released • A metal oxide is formed
Al aluminium ← (CARBON)			
Zn zinc			
Fe iron			
Sn tin		• No reaction	• No reaction
Pb lead		• No reaction	• No reaction
Cu copper ← (HYDROGEN)		• No reaction	• No reaction
Ag silver		• No reaction	• No reaction
Au gold	LEAST REACTIVE	• No reaction	• No reaction

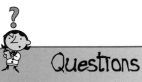

Did you know?

Tracing stolen gold is difficult because it can be melted and remoulded. But now we know that gold has its own 'fingerprint'. Trace elements found in the rocks around the gold make gold from different rocks unique. This means gold *can* be traced using this fingerprint. It also makes it difficult to fake gold.

You can make a reactivity series by seeing how vigorously they react with dilute acids (producing salts and hydrogen).

The top four elements in the list can only be displaced from their compounds by using electricity. Non-metals like carbon and hydrogen also form part of the reactivity series and are used to displace metals from their ores.

If a metal such as copper is put into a solution of a compound of a lower reactivity metal, like silver, a reaction happens:

copper + silver nitrate → copper nitrate + silver

Questions

1 What is reactivity?

2 Put these metals in order of reactivity with water: Mg, Cu, Ca, Ag, K, Zn, Fe, Na.

3 If zinc metal is put into silver nitrate solution, what is the reaction? Which metal is the more reactive?

4 How is the history of humans' use of metals related to the reactivity series?

Rocks, minerals, and ores

Minerals

Minerals are the stuff rocks are made of. A mineral is any solid element or compound found naturally. Examples are: diamond (carbon), quartz (silicon dioxide), and malachite (copper(II) carbonate).

Diamonds from rough 'stone' to 'rough cut' ... ready for finishing.

Minerals have been used by humans over thousands of years and one of the most common uses is as gemstones. Minerals are also used as pigments, ores for metals, and even as medicines.

Azurite is used as a pigment in paints.

A quartz crystal makes this watch work.

Ruby crystals are used in lasers.

Some uses of minerals

Minerals are crystalline substances. The size of the crystals depends on the conditions in which the mineral is formed. The shape of the crystals is another important factor. Some crystals are long, thin, and needle-like.

Many minerals crystallize under different conditions into different crystal forms.

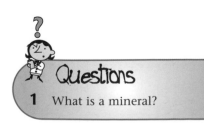

Questions

1 What is a mineral?

Rocks

Rocks are mixtures of minerals found in the Earth's crust. They can be formed by crystallization of minerals from a molten magma – igneous rocks. They can be recycled rocks and remains of dead organisms cemented together – sedimentary rocks. Rocks can be changed by high temperatures and pressure to form metamorphic rocks.

Ores

Minerals containing metals which can be extracted are called **ores**. There must be enough metal in the rock to make it worth the money it will cost to extract it.

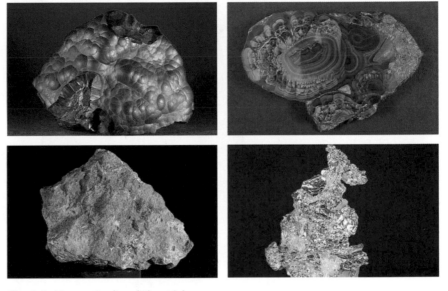

Top left: Haematite (iron(III) oxide).
Bottom left: Bauxite (aluminium oxide).
Top right: Malachite (copper(II) carbonate)
Bottom right: Natural (native) gold.

The reactivity of the metal affects how it can be used and how it can be extracted from the ore. Gold and silver ores are so unreactive that they can be found as the metal. This is called native metal. Aluminium is so reactive it needs heat and electricity to extract it from its ore. Iron and copper are not so reactive and can be extracted using heat and carbon.

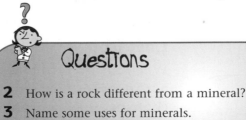

Questions

2 How is a rock different from a mineral?
3 Name some uses for minerals.
4 What is an ore and why are they important?

Ores from rock: extracting iron

Objectives

This spread should help you to

- know which ore the metal iron is extracted from
- know the reactions for extracting iron and about reduction and oxidation
- describe the different metals and elements used to make iron into steel

The extraction process

IN

Iron ore (haematite), coke (carbon), and limestone (to remove acidic impurities from slag)

A Iron(III) oxide reacts with the hot carbon monoxide to form iron and carbon dioxide.

| Iron(III) oxide (solid) | + | carbon monoxide (gas) | → | iron (liquid) | + | carbon dioxide (gas) |

$$Fe_2O_3(s) + 3CO(g) \longrightarrow 2Fe(l) + 3CO_2(g)$$

B Hot carbon dioxide reacts with more carbon to form carbon monoxide.

| carbon (solid) | + | carbon dioxide | → | carbon monoxide (gas) |

$$C(s) + CO_2(g) \longrightarrow 2CO(g)$$

C Coke is carbon which burns with oxygen to form carbon dioxide.

| carbon (solid) | + | oxygen (gas) | → | carbon dioxide (gas) |

$$C(s) + O_2(g) \longrightarrow CO_2(g)$$

Blast furnace for the extraction of iron

: removing oxygen from the metal oxide - the process of reduction

: carbon monoxide combines with oxygen from the ore - the process of oxidation

waste gases out

waste gases out

A
400 °C

B
800 °C

C
1400 °C

hot air in

hot air in

slag (liquid)

D

E

iron (liquid)

OUT

D Molten slag runs off and forms a solid used for road surfaces.

E Liquid iron runs off and is collected, some to solidify and the rest is taken off to make steel.

Cast iron

When the iron is allowed to set as a solid in a mould, it forms a hard, brittle metal. Having just come out of the furnace it contains a high amount of carbon, up to 4%. The solid iron is called cast iron. The shape is set in the mould so the iron forms the shape without needing to be bent.

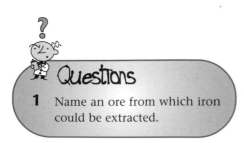

Questions

1 Name an ore from which iron could be extracted.

Cast iron has been used in the past for structures such as Ironbridge. It was opened in 1781 as the first iron bridge in the world.

Modern day uses of cast iron include cooking utensils.

Iron to steel

The molten iron from the blast furnace is run off and kept hot. It will be turned into steel. To do this most of the carbon and impurities left in the iron must be burnt off.

Scrap iron is added at this point to the molten iron. Then calcium oxide is added and a jet of oxygen blown through. The calcium oxide reacts with some impurities, forming a slag. Oxygen reacts with other impurities and some of the carbon. The iron becomes purer. Not all of the carbon is removed, just enough (about 1%) is left to make the iron very hard.

Finally other elements may be added to make a metal mixture called an alloy. The elements added change the properties of the steel and make it useful for different jobs.

An oxygen furnace for steelmaking.

Did you know?

Adding manganese, tungsten, or titanium makes the steel extremely hard. Adding chromium and nickel makes it stainless.

Name	Iron	Carbon	Other things added	Property	Use
Mild steel	99.5%	0.5%		Hard	Building car bodies
Hard steel	99.0%	1.0%		Very hard	Cutting blades
Duriron	84.0%	1.0%	15% silicon	Not affected by acid	Tanks/pipes in chemical factories

Questions

2 How is carbon dioxide used in a blast furnace?

3 What is cast iron and why it is different from steel?

4 Name some of the metals added to iron to make steel and describe their main properties.

Electrolysis

Objectives

This spread should help you to

- explain what electrolysis is
- describe how electrolysis is used in the alkali industry
- describe the conditions for electrolysis

Ionic compounds

Ionic compounds are made up of electrically charged particles called ions. In a solid ionic crystal such as sodium chloride (table salt) the ions are held very tightly. The ions can vibrate but not move about. The positive ions and negative ions are attracted to one another.

You can make an ionic solution by dissolving an ionic solid in water. In the solution the ions can move freely. The ions are surrounded by water molecules.

Electrocuting an ionic solution!

Ionic substance in water. Water particles collide with crystal and break it up.

Ionic substance has broken up into separate ions – electrically charged particles.

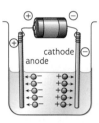

Pass electricity through the solution. Ions are attracted to electrodes

cathode
anode

Electrolysis.

If two rods of carbon (**electrodes**) are be placed in a beaker containing an ionic solution and connected by a battery, an electric current will flow through the solution. The electric current will cause a chemical change in the solution. This process is called **electrolysis**. The ionic solution conducts electricity because the ions are attracted to the oppositely charged electrode. The positive ions move towards the negative electrode (the **cathode**). The negative ions move towards the positive electrode (the **anode**). A solution containing ions is called an **electrolyte** because it conducts electricity.

Electrolysis of copper chloride

If you dissolve a crystal of copper(II) chloride in water, it separates into copper ions with a positive charge and chloride ions with a negative charge. This solution will conduct electricity. It is copper(II) chloride electrolyte.

If you put electrodes into the copper(II) chloride electrolyte and turn on the current, the ions are attracted to their opposite electrodes.

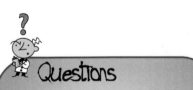

Questions

1 What is an ionic bond and how are the particles held together?

2 If an ionic substance is dissolved in water, what particles are formed?

3 Name two ways the product of electrolysis can be increased. Write a sentence about each.

At the cathode		
copper ion + electrons	→	copper metal atom
$Cu^{2+} + 2e^-$	→	Cu

At the anode		
chloride ion − electron	→	chlorine atom (molecule)
$Cl^- - 1e^-$	→	Cl (Cl_2)

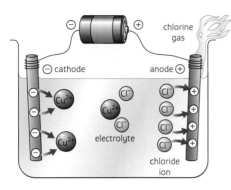

Electrolysis of copper(II) chloride.

Because the copper ions are attracted to the cathode (negative electrode), they are called **cations**. The copper ions combine with electrons from the cathode to form copper metal. A layer of copper metal is deposited on the cathode.

Chloride ions are attracted to the anode (positive electrode), so they are called **anions**. The chloride ions give up electrons to the anode and become chlorine atoms. The chlorine atoms join together to make molecules of chlorine gas.

Electrolysis of lead bromide

Here is what happens when you electrolyse lead bromide:

Electrolyte	Cation	Anion	Reaction at electrodes
lead bromide	lead ion	bromide ion	lead positive ion + 2 electrons → lead metal
$PbBr_2$	Pb^{2+}	$2Br^-$	$Pb^{2+} + 2e^- → Pb$
	$2Br^-$		2 bromine negative ions – 2 electrons → bromine gas $2\,Br^- – 2e^- → Br_2\,(g)$

More electrons – more electrolysis

The more electrons are pushed into the solution, the more ions can be changed to atoms. A measure of electron flow is current. So the bigger the current the more ions are changed into atoms and the bigger the mass of copper deposited at the electrode. For the copper chloride example:

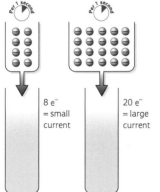

A bigger current means more product.

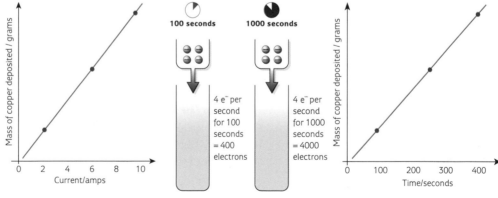

A longer time means more product.

If the same current flows for a longer time, more ions are changed into atoms. When a positive ion gains electrons to form an atom, the process is called **reduction**. When a negative ion loses electrons to form an atom, the process is called **oxidation**.

 **5.10**

Using electrolysis: metals

Objectives

This spread should help you to

- know electrolysis can be used for electroplating and extracting metal from ores
- describe how metals are electroplated
- describe how aluminium is extracted from its ore using electricity

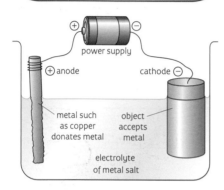

Electroplating.

Electroplating...

...with zinc   *...with chrome*   *...with tin*

...with rhodium.

silver plate
nickel surface

chromium plate
copper plate
iron surface

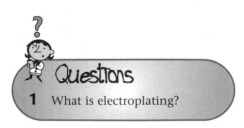

Silver atoms stick well to nickel, but chromium atoms need a layer of copper to make them stick to iron.

Questions

1. What is electroplating?

All the objects in the photographs have been coated with a thin layer of another metal. These coatings have two purposes. One is to make the object look decorative, the other is to protect the surface from corrosion.

To **electroplate** an object it is connected to one side of an electric supply, the cathode. The metal being used to supply the coating, for example copper, is connected to the other side of the electric supply, the anode.

The conducting solution (electrolyte) is a solution of a compound of the metal, such as copper(II) sulphate. As positive metal ions are attracted to the negative object, they gain electrons and form atoms. As the object is coated, the mass of metal deposited is exactly equal to the loss in mass of the anode. Copper can be purified using this method.

Extraction of aluminium

Aluminium is a very reactive metal. It reacts quickly with oxygen, forming a thin coating. This means the bond between aluminium and oxygen is very strong. The main aluminium ore is bauxite – largely aluminium oxide.

Heating with carbon does not provide enough energy to break the bonds between aluminium and oxygen. However, if aluminium oxide is dissolved in molten cryolite (a mineral), the ions are free to move. If an electric current is applied to the hot liquid the aluminium ions can move to the negative electrode (cathode).

A bauxite mine.

Aluminium is extracted from bauxite by electrolysis.

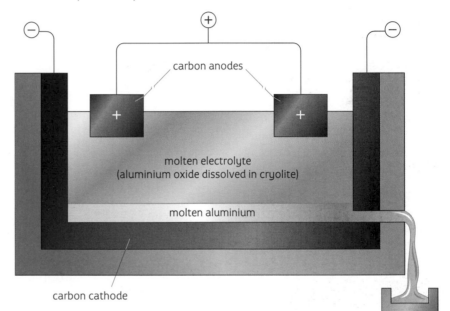

carbon anodes

molten electrolyte
(aluminium oxide dissolved in cryolite)

molten aluminium

carbon cathode

The aluminium ions become atoms and, in the heat, remain as molten metal. The metal is run off into moulds.

At the anode the oxide ions lose electrons to become oxygen atoms. These react with the hot carbon electrodes (which burn away easily) to form carbon dioxide.

Did you know?

A more efficient way of obtaining aluminium is to re-use aluminium metal. Recycling an aluminium can uses only 5% of the energy needed to make a new can and 9% of all household rubbish is drink cans.

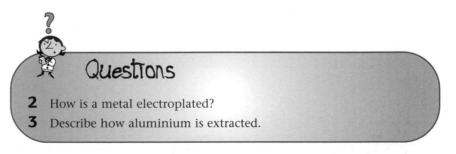

Questions

2 How is a metal electroplated?

3 Describe how aluminium is extracted.

Fire and combustion

Combustion is a chemical reaction where a gas combines with oxygen, giving out light and heat. It is an exothermic reaction.

Fire is uncontrolled combustion. The rate of reaction is so fast that there are flames and high temperatures.

Fires such as the one at King's Cross are dangerous not just because of the heat and flames. Other chemical reactions release dangerous gases such as hydrogen cyanide, hydrogen chloride, and carbon monoxide.

Daily Mail 56 PAGES TODAY

Vapour clue to the fireball on Tube escalator

FLASHPOINT OF DISASTER

The fire triangle

The fire triangle shows the three things necessary for a fire to go on burning. To put out a fire you must remove one of these three things.

▲ Water can be used to cool the fuel down and transfer the heat away from the exothermic reaction.

▲ Substances such as dry powder, foam, or carbon dioxide form a blanket that stops the fuel coming into contact with oxygen.

▲ The fuel can be removed: foresters cut firebreaks through forests so that if a fire starts in one place, it will stop when it runs out of fuel. The flames cannot jump over the firebreak.

A slow combustion reaction can be very dangerous. It may go unnoticed for a long time until it releases enough heat to become a serious fire. For example, someone may fall asleep with a lit cigarette and let the cigarette fall onto the bedding material. This can smoulder until it gets hot enough to burn or a draught of air blows oxygen over the smouldering material: then it bursts into flames.

exothermic reaction

oxygen gas

AIR HEAT

FUEL

e.g candle wax, wood, petrol

Rocket

- metal powder and metal salts
- gunpowder
- fuse
- gunpowder
- stick

FIReWORKS

In fireworks, chemicals burn fast in a confined space. The gases formed, and flames, escape from one end. In a rocket the gases rush out at the bottom, pushing the rocket upwards. In a Roman candle firework the gases escape upwards with sparks. The sparks are flakes of metal such as iron, magnesium, or aluminium that glow white hot. One notable feature of fireworks is the colours. These are caused by different metal ions in the flame

1 sodium: yellow

2 barium: brick red/yellow

3 strontium: bright red

4 copper: green

Flame test show that some elements burn with a characteristic colour. These elements also provide the colour in fireworks.

Combustion of a candle

When the wick of a candle is lit with a match, the wax melts, boils, and becomes a hot gas. This hot gas reacts with oxygen, releasing light and heat.

The candle continues to burn because the heat of the combustion reaction melts and boils more wax. It burns until all the wax has been used up, the oxygen is removed, or the wax is cooled down (by blowing on it, for instance) and becomes solid.

Talking point

Chip-pan fires, where the oil ignites, are very dangerous and a common cause of house fires. Why is it even more dangerous to try to extinguish these fires by pouring water on the pan?

Oxygen reactions

Objectives

This spread should help you to

- describe some oxidation reactions
- know the three ways fire can be stopped

Oxygen in everyday life

When a chemical combines with oxygen to make a new compound, it has been **oxidized**.

Some oxidations: respiration is the **oxidation** of glucose in a living thing; **combustion** is the burning of a material in oxygen; **rancidity** is the oxidation of fats during storage.

The extra work makes Jenni breathe faster. The extra oxygen is needed for ***respiration****.*

The bread is heated and catches on fire in the grill. This fire is the bread ***combusting*** *with oxygen.*

Oil on the metal chain of Jenni's bike not only makes it turn easily but slows down ***corrosion*** *or rusting.*

A special example of oxidation

Corrosion is the oxidation of metals in moist air. When iron or steel corrode it is called rusting. The iron compound formed pushes the metal atoms apart and weakens the attraction between them. This makes the structure weak. This can be very expensive in industry.

Aluminium also corrodes. But unlike iron, when aluminium oxidizes it does so only on the surface.

Fire is put out by stopping the combustion. This can be done by
- *blocking the oxygen*
- *cutting off the fuel*
- *getting rid of the heat.*

Questions

1 What is respiration?
2 What is a combustion reaction?
3 What element do respiration, combustion, and corrosion have in common?

More on corrosion

Corrosion is the oxidation of metals in moist air.

iron metal	+	oxygen gas	+	water vapour	⟶	iron(III) hydroxide
(solid)		(gas)		(gas)		(solid)

$$4Fe(s) + 3O_2(g) + 6H_2O(g) \longrightarrow 4Fe(OH)_3(g)$$

Corrosion prevention

To prevent corrosion costs a lot of money. Oxygen and water must be stopped from coming in contact with the iron (or steel). This can be done by painting, greasing or oiling, or coating with plastic, tin, chromium, or zinc. Another method is to use a more reactive metal attached to the iron. The more reactive metal reacts with the oxygen and corrodes. Because the iron is left uncorroded and the reactive metal corrodes away this method is known as sacrificial protection.

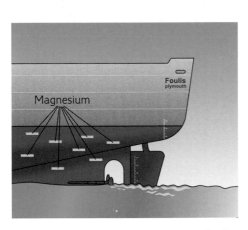

Magnesium blocks are used as sacrifical anodes to protect the ship's steel.

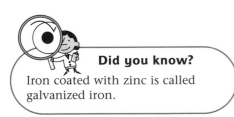

Did you know?

Iron coated with zinc is called galvanized iron.

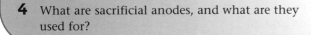

Left unprotected these pillars will corrode very quickly.

Questions

4 What are sacrificial anodes, and what are they used for?

5 When iron reacts with oxygen and water vapour what is the reaction?

5.13 # Acids, alkalis, and the pH scale

Objectives

This spread should help you to
- decribe the pH scale
- describe tests for acids and alkalis
- describe some common acids and alkalis

The pH scale

The pH scale is a measure of acidity. Acids have pH between 0 and 7. Alkalis have pH between 7 and 14. Water is neutral.

If you neutralize an acid like sulphuric or hydrochloric with an alkali like calcium hydroxide or sodium hydroxide, you will end up with a solution that has a pH of 7.

very acidic | very alkaline

Acids							Neutral			Alkalis				
0	1	2	3	4	5	6	7	8	9	10	11	12	13	14

The ph scale – a reaction is complete when the pH value is neutral

The pH of a solution can be measured using the colour change of dyes. Red litmus turns blue in an alkali. Blue litmus turns red in an acid.

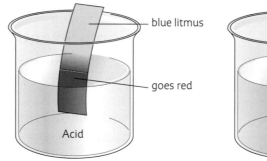

blue litmus — goes red — Acid

red litmus — goes blue — Alkali

Blue litmus goes red in an acid.   *Red litmus goes blue in an alkali.*

Universal indicator gives a more accurate idea of the pH.

Acids							Neutral			Alkalis				
0	1	2	3	4	5	6	7	8	9	10	11	12	13	14

Universal indicator colours.

You can also measure the pH using a pH meter.

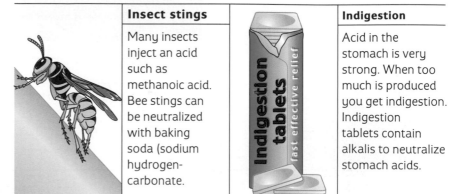

Insect stings	Indigestion
Many insects inject an acid such as methanoic acid. Bee stings can be neutralized with baking soda (sodium hydrogen-carbonate.	Acid in the stomach is very strong. When too much is produced you get indigestion. Indigestion tablets contain alkalis to neutralize stomach acids.

Questions

1 Draw the pH scale and add labels for very acidic, weakly acidic, neutral, weakly alkaline and very alkaline.

34

Acids and alkalis in everyday life

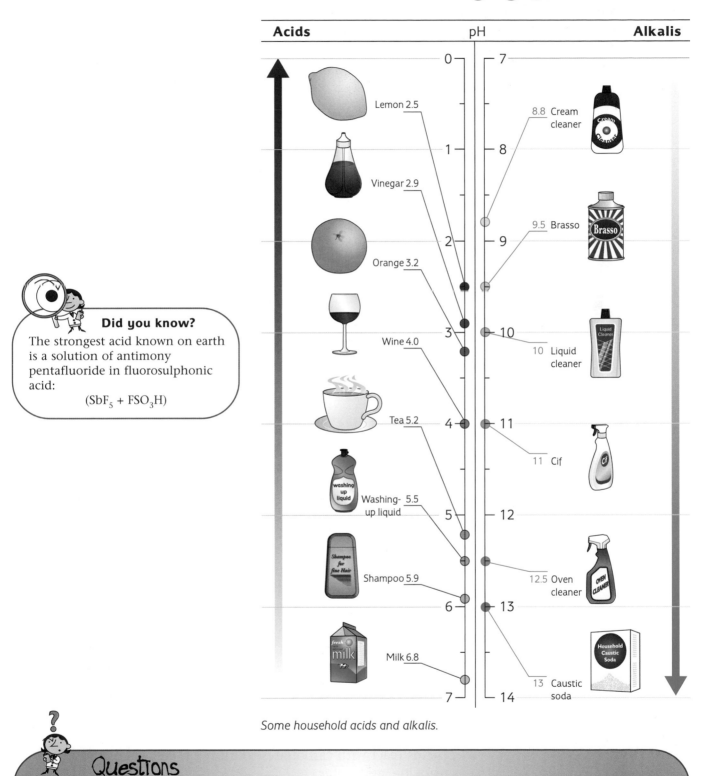

Did you know?

The strongest acid known on earth is a solution of antimony pentafluoride in fluorosulphonic acid:

$(SbF_5 + FSO_3H)$

Acids	pH	Alkalis
Lemon 2.5	0 — 7	8.8 Cream cleaner
Vinegar 2.9	1 — 8	9.5 Brasso
Orange 3.2	2 — 9	10 Liquid cleaner
Wine 4.0	3 — 10	11 Cif
Tea 5.2	4 — 11	12.5 Oven cleaner
Washing-up liquid 5.5	5 — 12	13 Caustic soda
Shampoo 5.9	6 — 13	
Milk 6.8	7 — 14	

Some household acids and alkalis.

Questions

2 Describe the reaction of an acid with an alkali.

3 Write down the reaction of sodium hydroxide with hydrochloric acid in words and symbols.

Acids and their reactions

Acid rain damages statues and buildings.

Did you know?

In equations, state symbols tell you what state the reactants and products are in.

(g) = gas

(l) = liquid

(s) = solid

(aq) = aqueous (in water)

Acid rain, rocks, and lakes

In Sweden the rain falls through clouds that contain many waste gases. These gases cross the North Sea from Britain. The rain dissolves the gases to form an acid. This **acid rain** falls on buildings and plants. It fills lakes and kills living things in the lakes.

One of the waste gases is sulphur dioxide. This dissolves to form sulphuric acid.

sulphur dioxide + water + oxygen ⟶ sulphuric acid

(gas)　　　　　(liquid)　(gas)　　　　　(liquid)

$$2SO_2(g) + 2H_2O(l) + O_2(g) \longrightarrow 2H_2SO_4(l)$$

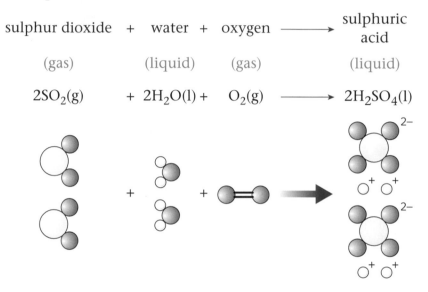

This sulphuric acid reacts with limestone which is calcium carbonate. It releases carbon dioxide and forms calcium sulphate, which is very soft, and flaky.

sulphuric acid + calcium carbonate ⟶ calcium sulphate + carbon dioxide + water

(aqueous)　(solid)　　　　　(solid)　　(gas)　(liquid)

$$H_2SO_4(l) + CaCO_3(s) \longrightarrow CaSO_4(s) + CO_2(g) + H_2O(l)$$

Acids react with carbonates to form a metal salt, carbon dioxide, and water.

acid + metal carbonate → metal salt + carbon dioxide + water

The acid in lakes or in the earth can be **neutralized** by adding lime. Lime is calcium hydroxide, an alkali.

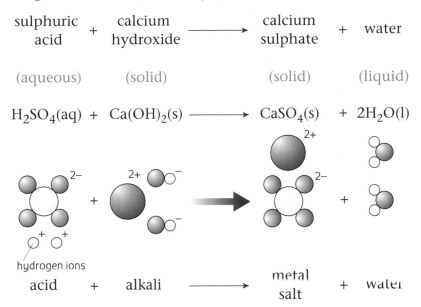

sulphuric acid	+	calcium hydroxide	→	calcium sulphate	+	water
(aqueous)		(solid)		(solid)		(liquid)

$$H_2SO_4(aq) + Ca(OH)_2(s) \longrightarrow CaSO_4(s) + 2H_2O(l)$$

hydrogen ions

| acid | + | alkali | → | metal salt | + | water |

What makes an acid acidic …?

The **acidity** is caused by the hydrogen ions that the acid releases when it dissolves in water. A strong acid is one like hydrochloric acid in which nearly all the acid molecules form ions. The more hydrogen ions (H^+), the more acidic the solution (lower pH).

hydrochloric acid	→	hydrogen ion	+	chloride ion
(aqueous)		(aqueous)		(aqueous)
HCl (aq)	→	H^+ (aq)	+	Cl^- (aq)

…And an alkali alkaline ?

Alkalis also break up when added to water. They form OH^- ions and the more OH^- ions, the more alkaline the solution.

sodium hydroxide	→	sodium ion	+	hydroxide ion
(aqueous)		(aqueous)		(aqueous)
NaOH (aq)	→	Na^+ (aq)	+	OH^- (aq)

Did you know?

'Aqueous' means 'dissolved in water'.

Questions

1 Describe the reaction of a metal carbonate with an acid.

Making salts

Objectives

This spread should help you to

- know acids can make salts by reacting with metals and bases
- know some salts are soluble while other are insoluble
- know some uses of salts

Sodium chloride is known as common salt but chemists use the word 'salt' to describe any metal compound made from acids.

Neutralization

You can make salts by **neutralization**. This is when an acid reacts with an alkali to form a salt and water.

$$\text{nitric acid} + \text{sodium hydroxide} \longrightarrow \text{sodium nitrate} + \text{water}$$

$$HNO_3(aq) + NaOH(aq) \longrightarrow NaNO_3(aq) + H_2O(l)$$

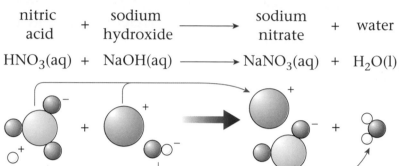

Ammonia in water forms the alkaline solution ammonium hydroxide. This can be neutralized to produce ammonium salts.

Acid + metal

Many metals are more reactive than hydrogen. When they are added to an acid the hydrogen is displaced and a metal salt is formed.

If zinc is added to an acid like sulphuric acid then zinc takes the place of hydrogen. Zinc sulphate is the metal salt formed and hydrogen gas is released.

$$\text{zinc metal} + \text{sulphuric acid} \longrightarrow \text{zinc sulphate} + \text{hydrogen}$$

$$Zn(s) + H_2SO_4(aq) \longrightarrow ZnSO_4(aq) + H_2(g)$$

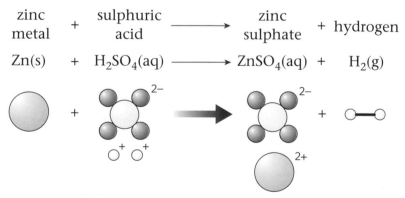

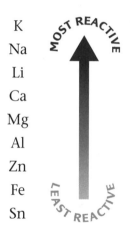

K
Na
Li
Ca
Mg
Al
Zn
Fe
Sn

MOST REACTIVE

LEAST REACTIVE

Acid + insoluble base

A base is any substance that can nutralize an acid. An alkali is a soluble **base**. Many transition metal oxides are insoluble bases. An oxide like black copper(II) oxide does not dissolve in water. But acids will still react with the oxide to form a metal salt.

Questions

1 Describe the reaction of an acid with a reactive metal.

2 What is neutralization?

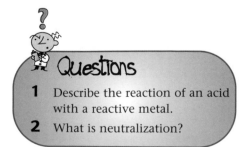

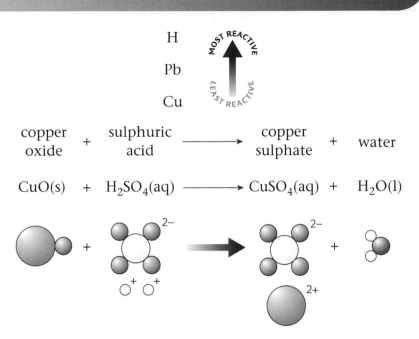

copper oxide + sulphuric acid ⟶ copper sulphate + water

$$CuO(s) + H_2SO_4(aq) \longrightarrow CuSO_4(aq) + H_2O(l)$$

Precipitation

Sometimes the metal ion and the compound ion are so
strongly attracted to each other that they will not break up.
This makes the salt insoluble. When an insoluble salt is
formed it is called a **precipitate**. This reaction can happen
when two metal salts are mixed together.

barium chloride + magnesium sulphate ⟶ barium sulphate + magnesium chloride

$$BaCl_2(aq) + MgSO_4(aq) \longrightarrow BaSO_4(s) + MgCl_2(aq)$$

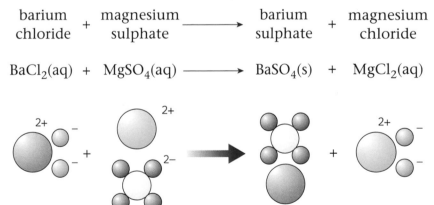

The barium sulphate forms a precipitate on the bottom of the
container. In the same way particles of mud sink to the
bottom of a pond or river.

Questions

3 What is the reaction of zinc with
hydrochloric acid?

4 What is the reaction of copper oxide with warm
sulphuric acid?

5 What is precipitation?

Many useful substances are not in themselves dangerous. But if they are used without knowledge of their properties or carelessly combined with other substances, they have the potential for creating dangerous situations that can cause human injury or death. Knowledge of these potential problems enables us to make full use of their other properties safely. When things go wrong, we should look carefully at the causes.

What happened on the day?

In Widget Inc.'s main manufacturing plant, they use hydrochloric acid to break down the waste in the sewage. On this day some of the acid had leaked. Workers spotted the leak, saw a potential danger, and rightly set out to neutralize the acid.

Adding an alkali to an acid neutralizes the acid. Bags of solid sodium hydroxide were kept at the plant for this purpose. The workers poured solid sodium hydroxide into the tank containing the hydrochloric acid. There was an explosion, which threw one of the firemen into the acid. He died as a result. Others near to the site suffered from breathing problems, nausea, and irritation to the eyes.

What do you think went wrong?

The Daily NEWS   Monday 22nd January

Firefighter dies, workers injured in factory blast

Safety in chemical plants

In a chemical plant it is important to cool containers in which an exothermic reaction occurs. This can be done using a heat exchanger. Water or another liquid flows through pipes that are either inside the reaction vessel or surround it. Heat from the reaction is transferred to the flowing liquid. This hot liquid can be transferred to another place in the chemical plant where it can be used to heat something.

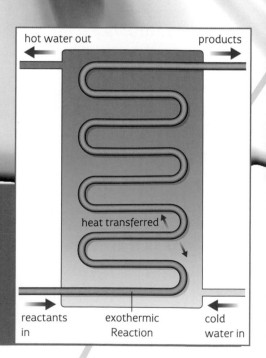

hot water out   products

heat transferred

reactants in   exothermic Reaction   cold water in

Why the explosion happened

To add alkali to acid is correct, but when this is done, huge amounts of energy are transferred. The reaction is very exothermic.

The transfer of large amounts of heat from the chemical reaction of

acid + alkali → salt + water

raises the temperature.

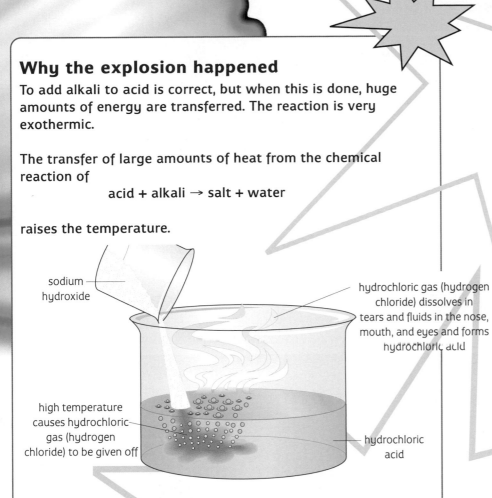

sodium hydroxide

hydrochloric gas (hydrogen chloride) dissolves in tears and fluids in the nose, mouth, and eyes and forms hydrochloric acid

high temperature causes hydrochloric gas (hydrogen chloride) to be given off

hydrochloric acid

Regrettably, although the bags of sodium hydroxide were kept for neutralizing acid, the workers did not read the instructions on the bags on how to use it.

How could the incident have been prevented?

It is possible to neutralize the acid without releasing so much heat. One way is to use a low-concentration solution of sodium hydroxide. If a 10% solution of sodium hydroxide is used, there is a lot of water to transfer the heat away from the hydrochloric acid. This is the instruction that the workers failed to read: they should have used a 10% solution of sodium hydroxide.

Another way is to use a safer reaction. Using sodium carbonate would neutralize the acid and produce carbon dioxide and sodium chloride. This reaction is much less exothermic.

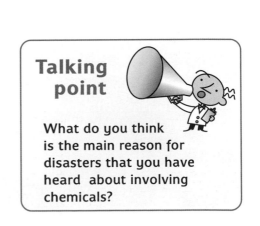

Talking point

What do you think is the main reason for disasters that you have heard about involving chemicals?

Elements and depression

Vincent van Gogh

Edgar Allan Poe

Many famous artists have been famous not only for their work. Edgar Allan Poe, a writer of horror stories, Vincent Van Gogh, a painter, and Kurt Cobain, the lead singer of Nirvana, are also famous for being manic depressives. Depression can often lead to suicide.

It was discovered 50 years ago that lithium carbonate helps to relieve certain types of depression. Nobody is quite sure how it works, but it does.

Kurt Cobain

Silicon – a semi-metal

An integrated circuit

Science fiction writers sometimes try to imagine lifeforms based on a different element from carbon. One possibility is silicon. Silicon can form similar compounds to carbon, but it is not as stable as carbon. It is, however, very useful in our everyday lives – as the silicon chip.

If you add a tiny amount of other elements to it, you can make it a conductor or an insulator: it is a semiconductor. Silicon can be used to make solid-state electronic devices, such as diodes, which allow an electric current to flow in one direction only, or transistors, which act like switches.

The inside of an integrated circuit

Using heat and chemical processes, an entire, complicated circuit containing thousands of transistors and other parts can be built on a single tiny piece of silicon. This is called an integrated circuit, or 'microchip'. Tiny gold wires are used to connect the integrated circuit to other circuits.

Silicon man!

HE'S IN HIS ELEMENT!

Americium and smoke

Smoke alarms go off when they detect smoke. One kind of smoke detector uses the radioactive element americium. This gives out particles because of its radioactivity. When these particles hit atoms of oxygen and nitrogen in the air, they knock electrons out of the atoms and make ions. In the detector is a pair of electrically charged plates, one positive and one negative. The ions move towards these plates. This flow of charged ions is an electric current. It flows all the time that the alarm is set.

Talking point

Some elements are more useful than others. Which do you think are the most used?

If smoke gets into the detector, some of the ions stick to the smoke particles. There are fewer ions flowing between the plates, so the current drops. This drop in current sets the alarm off.

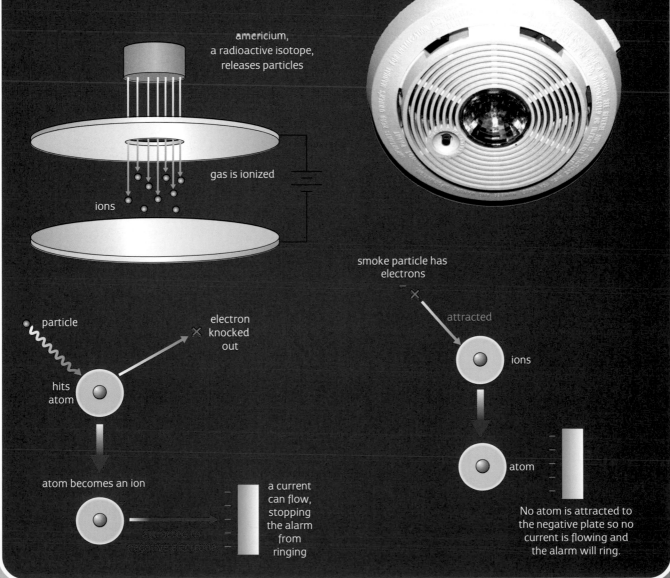

americium, a radioactive isotope, releases particles

gas is ionized

ions

smoke particle has electrons

attracted

ions

particle

electron knocked out

hits atom

atom

atom becomes an ion

a current can flow, stopping the alarm from ringing

attracted to negative electrode

No atom is attracted to the negative plate so no current is flowing and the alarm will ring.

Practice questions

1 Draw a table with two columns. Select from the general properties listed below those which apply to *metals*. Put these in the first column. Put the properties of *non-metals* in the second column.

Properties: brittle, sonorous, low melting points, high melting points, malleable, ductile, many are gases, shiny, have low densities, poor conductors of heat, good conductors of electricity, poor conductors of electricity.

2 The following is a paragraph about the metals in Group 1 of the Periodic Table. It contains *ten* mistakes. Write it out, correcting the mistakes.

'The first three Group 1 (alkaline earth) metals are lithium, sodium, and rubidium. They all have 3 electrons in their outer shells and decrease in size down the group. Unusually for metals, they have both high melting points and high densities, so that they float on water. They react vigorously with water giving off oxygen gas and forming an acid. The Group 1 metals are very reactive because their atoms easily gain one electron to become negative ions.'

3 Chromium, manganese, iron, nickel, and copper are well-known transition metals.

a List five properties common to all of them which make them 'typical metals'.

b Write down some uses of transition metals.

c Write down the name and the colour of one compound of each of the five metals.

d Transition metals (and their compounds) are often used as catalysts. What are catalysts?

4 a Make a larger copy of this outline of the Periodic Table:

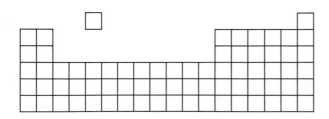

b Write in the group and period numbers.

c Draw a zigzag line to show how the metals are separated from the non-metals in the table.

d Now put the letters A to G in the correct places in the table, to fit these descriptions:

A The lightest element.
B Any noble gases.
C The most reactive alkali metal.
D The least reactive alkali metal.
E The most reactive halogen.
F A Group 3 metal.
G A transition metal.

5 Arrange the metals given below into a series with the most reactive at the top and the least reactive at the bottom. Write alongside each how it reacts with water and how it is found or extracted from its ore.

Metals: zinc, magnesium, gold, sodium

Reaction with water: fizzes, no reaction, very slow, reacts with steam

Obtained: found uncombined, extracted by smelting, extracted by electricity, extracted by electricity.

6 a What does the term *electrolysis* mean?

b Copy the diagram below, and label it using the words in this list, which are all connected with electrolysis:

anode, cathode, electrolyte

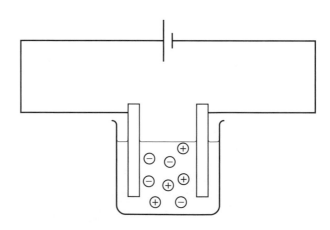

7 Which of the following metals is most likely to be found in its natural state? Tin, lead, iron, gold, calcium, sodium.

8 Why is aluminium extracted by electrolysis and not in a blast furnace?

9 Only a few elements are found uncombined in the Earth's crust. Gold is one example. The rest occur as compounds, and have to be extracted from their ores. This is usually carried out by heating with carbon, or by electrolysis.

Some information about the extraction of different metals is shown below.

Metal	Formula of main ore	Method of extraction
Iron	Fe_2O_3	Heating with carbon
Aluminium	$Al_2O_3.2H_2O$	Electrolysis
Copper	Cu_2S	Roasting the ore

a Give the chemical name of each ore.

b Arrange the four metals in order of reactivity.

c How are the more reactive metals extracted from their ores?

d i How is the least reactive metal extracted from its ore?

ii Why can't this method be used for the more reactive metals?

e Iron and aluminium ores are relatively cheap, but aluminium metal is a lot more expensive than iron metal. Why is this?

f Which of the methods would you use to extract:

i potassium?

ii lead?

iii magnesium?

(Hint: look at the reactivity series)

g Gold is a metal found native in the Earth's crust. Explain what *native* means.

h Where should gold go, in your list for **b**?

i Name another metal which occurs native.

10 a Draw a diagram of the blast furnace. Show clearly on your diagram:

i where air is 'blasted' into the furnace;

ii where the molten iron is removed;

iii where the second liquid is removed.

b i Name the three raw materials added at the top of the furnace.

ii What is the purpose of each material?

c i What is the name of the second liquid that is removed from the bottom of the furnace?

ii When it solidifies, does it have any uses? If so, name one.

d i Name a waste gas that comes out at the top of the furnace.

ii Does this gas have a use? If so, what?

e Write an equation for the chemical reaction which produces the iron.

11 State whether the following properties apply to acids, alkalis or both:

a form ions when dissolved in water

b have pH values less than 7

c have pH values greater than 7

d react with magnesium releasing hydrogen

e dissolve carbonates releasing carbon dioxide

f form OH(aq) ions

g change the colour of universal indicator

h may be strong or weak

i are corrosive

j are good for removing grease

12 What are:

a the pH scale

b the pH value of water

c neutralization

d precipitation?

13 a Zinc and iron are metals. Both react with dilute hydrochloric acid.

i Name 2 properties which you would expect metals such as zinc and iron to have.

ii Explain how you would find out which of these 2 metals reacted most quickly with dilute hydrochloric acid.

b Copper, iron and aluminium are economically important metals. Give an example in each case of an every-day use.

c The figures in the table show the percentage corrosion (reaction) of some steel bars placed in solutions of various acidities, measured as units of pH.

% corrosion of steel bars	65	60	55	50	20	15	10
pH of solution	1	2	3	4	5	6	7

i Draw a graph of % corrosion against pH using the figures in the table.

ii A solution of pH 4 causes 50% corrosion of the steel bars. Explain what you would do to change the pH to give a solution which was less corrosive.

14 Name the substances formed when the following chemicals react together:

a hydrochloric acid and sodium carbonate

b sulphuric acid and sodium hydroxide.

Key words

alkali metals   metal element in group 1 of periodic table

alloy   a mixture of two or more metals or a metal mixed with anon metal e.g. carbon

anode   the positive electrode

base   a substance that reacts with an acid to form a salt and water

boiling point   the temperature a liquid turns into a gas

cathode   the negative electrode

combustion   when a substance reacts with oxygen to produce light and heat often with flames

conductors   allows electricity and heat to pass through very quickly

corrosion   when a metals combines with oxygen

ductile   metal drawn into a thin wire

electrodes   the poles at which a substance is connected to electricity – positive and negative

electrolysis   when a substance is broken down using electricity

electrolyte   the liquid which allows electricity to flow through

element   a substance made up of only one type of atom, cannot be split up into simpler substances by chemical reactions

electroplate   when electricity is used to transfer a metal coating onto another metal

malleable   metal hammered into a thin sheet

metals   elements that are shiny, good conductors of electricity and heat and react with acids to release hydrogen

metalloid an element which has characteristics of a metal and non-metal

melting point the temperature a solid melts into a liquid

neutralization when a base and an acid react to form a salt and water

ores a mineral or rock containing metals that can be extracted

oxidation (i) when an element combines with oxygen to form an oxide

(ii) when a negative ion loses electrons to form an atom

periodic table the arrangement of elements in order of atomic number, having groups and periods

precipitate when a solid is formed in a chemical reaction

pure a substance that contains only one sort of particle

reactivity series a list of element in order of chemical reactivity

relative formula mass the mass of each atom in a substance formula added together, in g.

reduction when a positive ion gains electrons to form an atom

salt one of the products when a base neutralizes an acid

synthesis when chemicals join together to form a new substance

transition metals a metal in the central block of the periodic table

Earth materials

To us the Earth seems very firm and solid. Yet there are volcanoes that throw out molten rock and earthquakes where the earth moves. The earth is a 'living' body continually undergoing change. It's very different now to the way was when it was formed billions of years ago.

Module 6

Limestone

Objectives

This spread should help you to

- describe how limestone is formed
- describe why limestones are different
- know how limestone is changed to form synthetic rock

Shelly limestone. Powdered Limestone can be used to neutralize acidity in lakes and soils

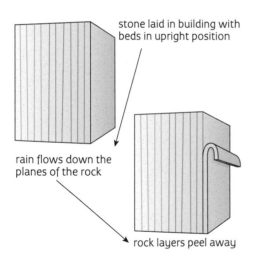

stone laid in building with beds in upright position

rain flows down the planes of the rock

rock layers peel away

Blocks laid in this way will weather more quickly than those laid horizontally.

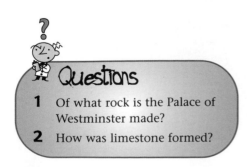

Questions

1 Of what rock is the Palace of Westminster made?

2 How was limestone formed?

Limestone – a tale of two buildings

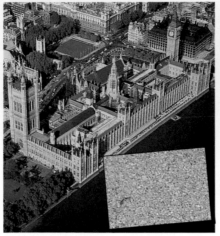

The Palace of Westminster.   *St Paul's Cathedral.*

Any visitor to London will have seen one or both of these buildings. They may not know that they are both made of limestone: but two different types of limestone.

The Palace of Westminster, also known as the Houses of Parliament, has been standing for over 100 years but 40% of its stone has been replaced. The rock is soft enough to carve but hard enough to withstand the weather. So why has so much worn away? The answer is in the rock used and the way it was used.

Some limestone is formed from tiny shells cemented together by chemicals. If the shells are too big then the rock is weakened. The shells break up and fall out, leaving holes. Water gets into these holes, freezes, and expands, cracking the rock. This makes the rock softer.

Another reason for the break up of the rock is poor building. To use the strength of the rock the layers need to be laid in the same way as in the rock layer. If not, rainwater can get into the layers and peel them off.

St Paul's Cathedral is a different story as the rock chosen was Portland stone. This was formed during a time when life in the ancient seas was limited. Tiny particles of calcium carbonate precipitated out of the sea water. These round particles, called oolites, were cemented together by more calcium carbonate. This makes a harder limestone. Many of the masons who built St Paul's knew their trade and most blocks were laid with the layers in the right direction.

Cement, concrete, and mortar

Not all limestone quarried can be used for building stone. Some has too many shells or is too soft but it can be used for making other building materials, like cement.

Limestone can be converted by thermal decomposition, to quicklime (calcium oxide - giving of carbon dioxide) in a kiln. It can then be further changed into **slaked lime** (calcium hydroxide) by adding water.

Cement is a mixture of calcium and aluminium compounds. It is made with slaked lime. On setting, the calcium hydroxide gives up water and reacts with carbon dioxide in the air. Long crystals of calcium carbonate form, binding the mass together.

Concrete is cement mixed with sand, small stones, and water. Again, the calcium hydroxide loses water and reacts with carbon dioxide in the air. This forms long calcium carbonate crystals. Because of the large stones it contains, concrete is not very strong. To make it stronger, steel rods or mesh are laid in the mixture.

Mortar is a mixture of slaked lime, sand, and water mixed into a paste. When put between bricks, the same reaction as for cement occurs, binding the sand and bricks together.

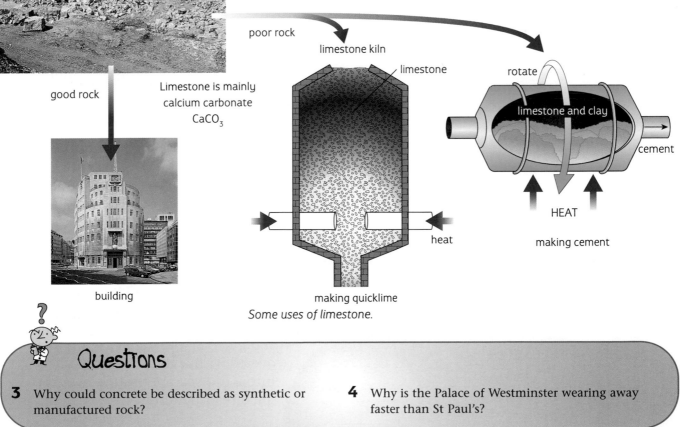

poor rock

good rock

Limestone is mainly calcium carbonate $CaCO_3$

building

limestone kiln

limestone

heat

making quicklime

rotate

limestone and clay

cement

HEAT

making cement

Some uses of limestone.

Questions

3 Why could concrete be described as synthetic or manufactured rock?

4 Why is the Palace of Westminster wearing away faster than St Paul's?

Glass, ceramics, and other composites

Glass

Glass has been around for a very long time. Romans used glass to make many beautiful objects.

The materials used to make glass are sand, metal oxides, and chemicals to make it coloured, stronger, or decorative.

Sand is silica, silicon dioxide. It is mixed with metal carbonates such as sodium carbonate, calcium carbonate, or magnesium carbonate. The mixture is heated to a very high temperature. The carbonates break down to form oxides and react with the sand.

The molten glass produced can be cooled or kept hot and worked into an object. If heated, silica cools to form an ordered crystal. In glass the presence of the metals sodium, calcium, and magnesium make the liquid form a disordered structure when it cools. Glass is like a thick liquid. Over a very long period of time it will flow. Glass is known as a **super-cooled liquid**.

To colour the glass, metal ions such as chromium, cobalt, or uranium are added. Natural glasses can be formed around volcanoes as obsidian. Lightning can melt sand into glass tubes called fulgurites. Meteorites bring glass in from outer space.

Glass can be recycled by heating it up, forming a molten liquid that can be added to a new glass mixture.

Ceramics

Bricks, tiles, mugs, and flowerpots are made from clay. Clay is silica mixed with other minerals such as aluminium compounds. Wet clay can be moulded. The silica crystals move over each other and set in place when a shape is formed. To keep the moulded shape, the object is heated. The silica forms a glass that bonds the minerals together.

Porcelain is clay fired at a very high temperature so that a hard silica surface is formed. To colour or put a picture on the object, it is painted with pigments. The pigments are then covered with a glaze which hardens into a transparent coating over the picture or pattern.

Composites

Composites are materials designed to have special properties. Bone is a natural composite. It consists of calcium phosphate cement with long fibres of the protein collagen in it.

Fibreglass is a man-made composite that uses glass fibres in a plastic resin. The resin sets hard, trapping the glass fibres. This makes a hard, shiny, light material that can be used for making boats, car bodies, and other objects.

Modern professional tennis rackets are made from a composite material in which carbon fibres are trapped in epoxy resin, forming a strong rigid plastic. Carbon fibres are stiff and strong, but they are lighter than other fibres. This type of composite material is good at absorbing shock, which protects the player from injury or tennis elbow.

Chemists are producing more materials known as 'smart' materials:

- Optical fibres that transmit light along a fibre.
- Piezoelectric plastics and ceramics that change shape when an electric current is passed through them. Squeezing them creates an electric field.
- Shape-memory alloys – mixtures of metals that return to their original shape when heated or bent.
- Polymer gels made from long carbon chains cross-linked into a network. The spaces are filled with oil or water. These gels stretch or swell by absorbing water. They are used in disposable nappies and feminine hygiene products.
- Photochromic solids that darken when exposed to light, like the lenses in some sunglasses.
- Liquid crystals which are made from long carbon chains. These change colour and shape when heated or when electricity is passed through them. They have been used in climbing ropes which change colour when overloaded.

Talking point

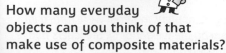

How many everyday objects can you think of that make use of composite materials?

Fossil fuels

Objectives

This spread should help you to
- know what a fossil fuel is
- describe where they have come from
- describe how oil is found and extracted

All these pictures are linked by the theme of **fossil fuels**.

When plants and animals of millions of years ago died their remains were covered by swamps or mud in the seas. This stopped air getting to them. These layers prevented the total decay and break up of the remains of these plants and animals.

The plant material formed a black solid, rich in carbon and hydrogen, with some oxygen and sulphur. This is **coal**. In wet conditions where plant and animal remains were mixed up, oil and gas formed.

September 2000 in France, Belgium, and Britain. Oil refineries and distribution centres were blockaded by angry people complaining about high oil prices.

The air is thick with mist, smells of rotting vegetation, that sulphurous cabbage-like stench. There are sounds of bellowing animals and heavy feet running through water. It is millions of years ago. The land is covered with fern-like trees, and dinosaurs roam, searching for food.

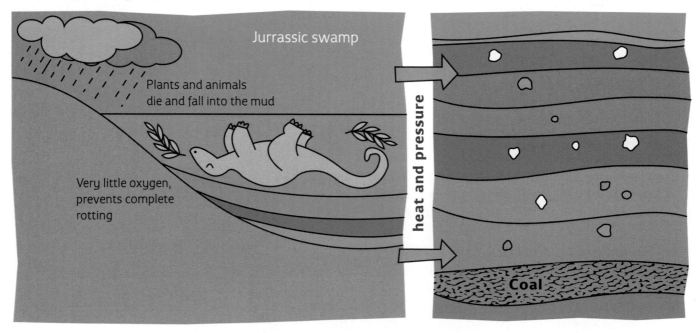

Jurrassic swamp

Plants and animals die and fall into the mud

Very little oxygen, prevents complete rotting

heat and pressure

Coal

Layers of plant material were turned into coal by the weight of all the layers above pressing on them,

Oil and gas contain mainly compounds of carbon and hydrogen. (Compounds containing *only* carbon and hydrogen are called **hydrocarbons**.)

Finding and extracting oil and gas

Over millions of years the mud, sand, and silt of ancient seabeds formed layers of sedimentary rock. Oil and gas became trapped in rock caverns or in areas of porous rock.

Fossil fuels are scarce and it has been estimated that all the oil will soon be used up. Geologists search for dome-shaped rock layers that could contain oil. These are called **anticlines**.

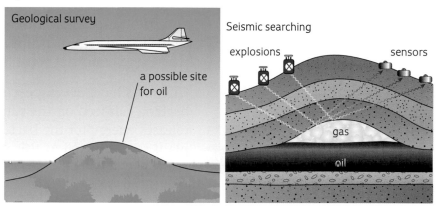

Searching for oil.

A gusher.

To look beneath the surface, geologists explode charges on the rock surface. These explosions send waves down through the rocks. They bounce off the surface of the layers. These reflected waves are collected by sensors and give a picture of the rocks beneath. The last stage is to drill a test hole or exploratory drill.

If oil is present it could be under great pressure from the rocks pushing down on the dome. If it is, then it gushes to the surface. The oil drill hole is capped so that the oil well can give up its oil more slowly.

Much of the world's oil has been found in remote areas so it has to be collected and transported using huge oil tanker ships. The oil is taken to refineries where the useful parts are separated.

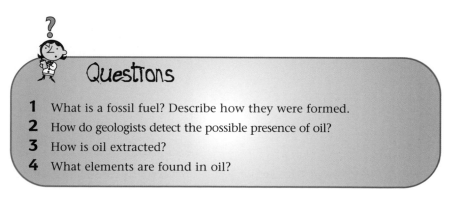

Questions

1   What is a fossil fuel? Describe how they were formed.
2   How do geologists detect the possible presence of oil?
3   How is oil extracted?
4   What elements are found in oil?

Burning fuels and the air

London smog in the 1950s was caused by coal-burning power station and fires.

Fossil fuels such as coal and oil are a mixture of hydrocarbons, with some sulphur and nitrogen compounds. Burning petrol, diesel, and coal produces carbon, sulphur, nitrogen oxides and water (vapour). About 1.6% of United Kingdom coal is sulphur. The sulphur and nitrogen come from the remains of living organisms and from minerals.

Burning coal

When coal burns, it produces carbon oxides, nitrogen oxides, and sulphur oxides. These go into the air and dissolve in rain to form acid rain. It is not a new problem but it is getting worse and countries have laws regulating emissions.

Chemists have developed methods of cleaning coal. Certain bacteria can feed on the sulphur and some of the minerals. This releases energy for the bacteria. Sardinia has set up an industrial plant to clean coal in this way.

Removing nitrogen is not so easy. In power stations it can be done by injecting ammonia into the flue gases. At certain temperatures the ammonia removes the nitrogen oxides by turning them into nitrogen and water which escape into the atmosphere.

Burning petrol and diesel oil

Most modern vehicles have one of two types of engine: diesel and petrol. Both are internal combustion engines which explode a compressed fuel in a cylinder.

The expansion of car use in 1970s led to congested roads and poor quality air

Emissions from car-exhaust pipes cause air pollution. Modern cars are monitored to make sure their emissions are not too high

Both types of engine produce carbon monoxide (but diesel produces only 10% of what the petrol engine produces). Both produce sulphur and nitrogen oxides. Diesel engines produce a large amount of carbon particles. Diesel engines are more efficient than petrol engines and produce less carbon dioxide per mile.

Catalysts can be used to reduce the problem of emission from internal combustion engines. Diesels are more difficult than petrol engines because of the carbon particles. To remove these, filters are used but they need frequent changing. The use of catalysts for cleaning emissions continues to develop.

MOT Exhaust Emissions Test Results:
Catalyst equipped vehicle with closed loop control

Test Station: ANYTOWN GARAGE Tel: 0101 267691 Station No: AB 6767
UNIT 1, NEW STREET, EREWHON, OLDSHIRE OD1 2BC

Software release: Ver 8.0   Database release: August 2000

Date of Test: Mon Mar 12 2001   Time of Test: 10:27

Vehicle Details

Vehicle Registration:	MN1 0UP
Vehicle Manufacturer	FORD
Vehicle Model:	Fiesta Engine Type HCS
Engine Capacity:	1100
Odometer Reading:	45388

DESCRIPTION	Limits	Reading	
		82°C	PASS
Engine oil temp	Min 80°C		**PASS**
Fast Idle Test:		3061 rpm	Pass
Engine Speed	2750-3150 rpm	0.01%	Pass
CO	max 0.30%	10 ppm	Pass
HC	max 200 ppm	1.00	Pass
Lambda	0.95-1.09		**PASS**
Natural Idle Test:		908 rpm	Pass
Engine Speed	800-1000 rpm	0.00%	Pass
CO	max 0.50%		

Exhaust Emission Test: **PASS**

Overall Result: Signature: *M Mechanic*

Tested By: M Mechanic

Copy of an emission report on a car in an MOT

Exhaust emission	Old style petrol	Lean burn petrol	Lean burn diesel
Oxygen	0.5%	12%	16%
Hydrocarbons	250 ppm	100 ppm	75 ppm
Carbon monoxide	0.7%	0.2%	0.03%
Nitrogen oxide	3200 ppm	300 ppm	130 ppm
Carbon dioxide	14%	6%	4%
Water	10%	6%	6%

ppm = parts per million

Education in Chemistry, Vol 37, No. 5, Sept 2000

Questions

1 What is combustion?

2 What are the two main elements found in a fossil fuel?

3 What waste gases are formed when a fossil fuel burns?

4 Why are petrol-burning cars considered so dangerous to the atmosphere?

Chemicals from crude oil

Objectives

This spread should help you to
- describe fractional distillation
- describe cracking
- know why cracking is needed

Un-mixing a mixture

Crude oil is heated at the bottom of a distillation column until it boils. The vapour is fed into the column. As the vapour rises, different parts (called **fractions**) cool and become liquid. This liquid is drawn off. Each hydrocarbon vapour group turns to a liquid at a different temperature. This process is known as **fractional distillation**. It is a way of refining *crude* oil.

more flammable

HEAT

crude oil

more viscous

40°C

110°C

180°C

250°C

340°C

No. of carbon atoms	Molecule example	Named
$C_1 - C_4$ small molecules		Petroleum gas
$C_4 - C_{12}$		Petrol or gasoline
$C_{12} - C_{15}$		Kerosine
$C_{15} - C_{19}$		Diesel
$C_{20} - C_{30}$		Lubricating oils
$C_{30} - C_{40}$		Fuel oil
$C_{40} - C_{50}$		Paraffin wax
C_{50} and above		Bitumen

An oil fractionating column. The oil is heated until it boils. The vapour is fed into a column. as the vapour rises different parts get cold and it becomes a liquid. This liquid is drawn off. Each liquid group turns to a liquid at different temperatures as shown

The smaller molecules, such as petrol, are the ones in greatesst demand. Unfortunately this group of compounds is also one of the smallest amounts produced. Smaller molecules have low boiling points and can vapourize more easily. They are more volatile and burn more easily than long chain molecules.

Cracking

Long chain molecules become tangled up. Because of this they form thick syrupy liquids. They are more viscous and less volatile than hydrocarbons with small molecules. To obtain small molecules from big molecules, the big ones have to be broken up. This is called **cracking**.

The big molecules have very strong attractive forces so will not break up easily. To help the reaction a catalyst is used. This speeds up the reaction by lowering the activation energy for the reaction.

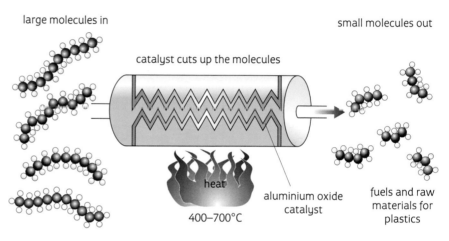

Cracking oil - thermal decomposition at work.

When the long chains are broken into shorter chains the molecules produced also contain some useful chemicals for making plastics.

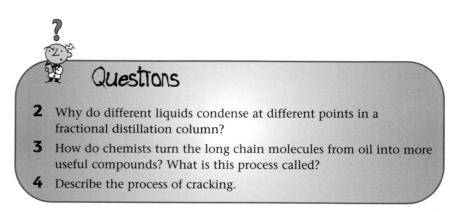

Questions

2 Why do different liquids condense at different points in a fractional distillation column?

3 How do chemists turn the long chain molecules from oil into more useful compounds? What is this process called?

4 Describe the process of cracking.

Building chains: plastics

Objectives

This spread should help you to

- know how plastics are formed
- describe some of the uses of plastics

Plastics old and new

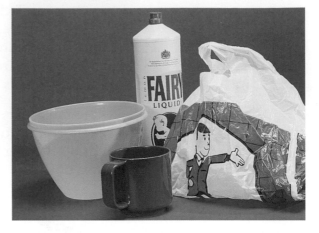

Plastics are all around us. This picture shows only a few of the objects made from plastics. Not all plastics are the same. There are many different varieties of plastics.

Living in the 1920s...   *...and today.*

These two homes are very different, separated by 80 years. It is not only the activities and the style that differ, but the materials being used. The 1920s home contains a lot of natural materials like woollen or cotton fabrics and wood, while the modern home contains a lot of synthetic fabrics and plastics.

Questions

1 Name some of the common uses for plastics.

The polys...

Polythene is used for plastic bags, bottles, and containers.

Propene, which forms poly(propene), used for crates, ropes, floor coverings, and car bumpers.

Any visit to a fast food restaurant will produce a polystyrene container. Plastics can be formed as fibres which, like wool or cotton, can be spun into materials. Polyvinyl chloride (PVC) is another plastic you may have heard of.

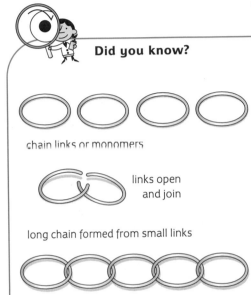
Monomers ...

The small molecules used to make long chain molecules are called **monomers**. Imagine a chain link. To form a chain these links have to be split and re-linked.

To break the monomers so that they can link up takes a lot of energy. If catalysts are used, the activation energy can be lowered.

... to polymers

The reaction of 'joining' monomers is called **polymerization** and the longer or bigger molecule is called a **polymer**. An example is ethene forming poly(ethene), or polythene as we more commonly know it.

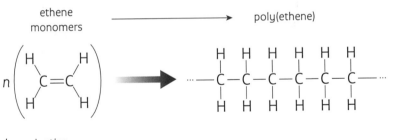

Polymerization.

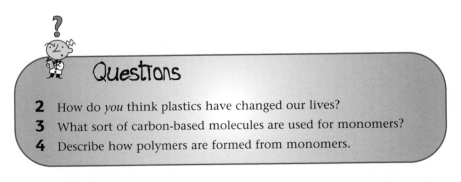

Questions

2 How do *you* think plastics have changed our lives?

3 What sort of carbon-based molecules are used for monomers?

4 Describe how polymers are formed from monomers.

Homes of the future

The shell – walls

With the development of plastics, it is possible that house walls could be made from plastic. At present only between 5% and 8% of the total material used in buildings is plastic.

If plastics are used, they will be composites. Strong, light, and resistant to corrosion and weather, they will be practically maintenance free. Careful use of plastics will make them fire resistant. Already, in Finland, chemists have built a house entirely of plastic.

Solar cells for electricity

The roof

A roof keeps out rain, snow, and so on, but it could easily be adapted to contain solar panels.

Inside the solar panel, photochemical reactions would be used to produce electricity. Another part of the solar panel can be made of highly absorbent plastic with water pipes.

Heat would be trapped in the panel, and the black plastic pipes would absorb the heat. The temperature of the water in the pipes would go up.

The heat produced can be used in the house. The hot water can be used in the house or used to heat ceramic materials which would store heat to be released at night. Part of the roof could even be used as a garden for growing plants.

Smart solar cells could be made that turn to catch all of the sunlight and make use of even small amounts of light to produce electricity.

Altogether these ideas could reduce the energy costs by 30% to 50%, compared to burning fossil fuels.

Solar cells for heating water (angled to the sky)

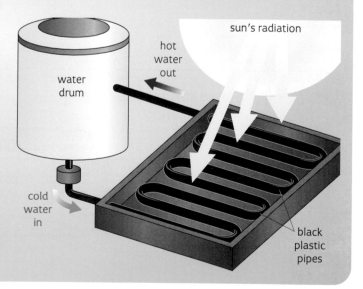

water drum

hot water out

sun's radiation

cold water in

black plastic pipes

A 'garden house' has added insulation and less impact on the environment.

Inside the house

The use of liquid crystals, and more recently plasma display technology, has allowed the development of flat screens, so one wall could be a television screen. This screen could be linked to the computer, televisions, movie centre, and telephones.

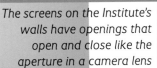

Large, flat, plasma television screens.

The computer would control the appliances in the house. Waste would be automatically recycled. The windows would have screens that open and close as the light changes. Indeed the whole house would turn with the sun to use as much of the light as possible.

Are all of these ideas beyond belief? Not all of them. There are examples of 'smart' houses around the world such as:

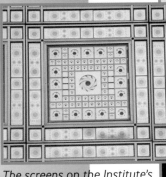

The screens on the Institute's walls have openings that open and close like the aperture in a camera lens

The Arab Institute

- The designer Jean Nouvel's glass-fronted Arab Institute in Paris, which has screens that open and close with sun intensity
- Jan Kaplicky's houses in Toulouse, which use ceramic materials that store heat energy
- Richard Hordern's Wing Tower that turns with the sun, built for Glasgow's millennium celebrations
- Wolfram Popp's Pixel Park in Berlin, which has moveable translucent walls that become television screens on the command of a computer

Talking point

What do you think would be the most important feature of a future house to come from the world of chemistry?

More rubbish

Archaeology's treasure trove

Humans have always produced waste and for archaeologists the rubbish tip is a valuable site. What was thrown away can tell the archaeologist about how people lived, their technology, what they ate, and the things they made.

Yesterday's rubbish – an archaeologist's treasure!

Getting rid of the rubbish

There is much debate about the best way of doing this. One solution is to do more recycling of materials like paper, metal, glass, and textiles. Another solution is to burn the waste in large incinerators to produce heat and electricity. A criticism of these incinerators is that they produce waste gases. A third solution is to use a landfill site.

It is unlikely that one method will solve the problem. The solution is more likely to be a combination of recycling, incineration, and landfill but with careful selection of materials.

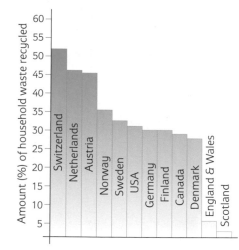

Recycling by countries.

A landfill site.

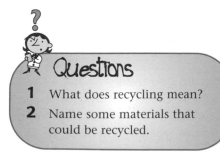

Questions

1 What does recycling mean?
2 Name some materials that could be recycled.

Landfill sites

Today rubbish tips or landfills are huge and becoming a problem. Each year in the UK alone about 29 million tonnes of rubbish are produced. That is half a tonne of rubbish per person. Over 90% of that rubbish ends up being buried in landfills.

In a landfill site, **non-biodegradable** materials, like some plastics such as polythene, do not rot or break down. **Biodegradable** materials can be broken down by microorganisms. In a landfill site these will decompose or break down producing chemicals that return to the soil.

One danger with decomposition is that bacteria produce gases. This is about 55% methane (highly combustible and explosive), 44% carbon dioxide (a greenhouse gas which could contribute to global warming). There are also small amounts of carbon monoxide, hydrogen, hydrogen sulphide, and other gases. One litre of rubbish over 10 years can produce 100 litres of gas.

Burning off methane gas on an old landfill site

Another danger of landfills is that they produce polluted liquid which can flow into surrounding soil and water and enter plants and animals. To prevent this, landfill sites are lined with clay and polymer sheets. The liquid is channelled to pumps which pump it to treatment plants.

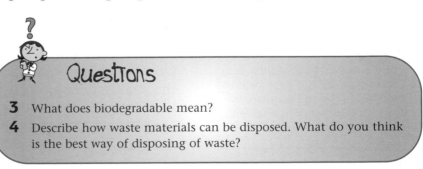

Questions

3 What does biodegradable mean?

4 Describe how waste materials can be disposed. What do you think is the best way of disposing of waste?

Objectives

This spread should help you to

- explain the role of ozone in the atmosphere
- describe what the greenhouse effect is
- describe the chemicals that destroy the ozone layer

Low temperatures cause water to condense. In these cold clouds chlorine and bromine from industry react with ozone, decreasing it and creating the ozone hole

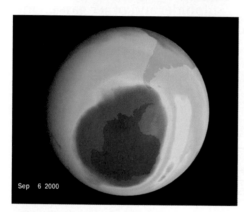

Since 1985 scientists have detected a hole in the ozone layer over Antarctica. During the year this hole changes size, usually bigger in spring because of the cold winter reactions. It is now more than three times the size of the USA.

Did you know?

Paul Crutzen, Mario Molina, and Sherwood Rowland were awarded the Nobel Prize in chemistry in 1995 for their work in unravelling the story of the ozone layer.

The ozone hole

ozone is formed by ultraviolet radiation acting on oxygen

ozone is broken down

Ultraviolet radiation breaks down chlorofluorocarbons, releasing chlorine atoms. Chlorine atoms react with ozone, producing oxygen and chlorine

nitrogen oxide + ozone → nitrogen dioxide + oxygen

chlorofluorocarbons

chlorofluorocarbons

stratosphere

troposphere

Plastic foams, aerosols, and fridges in the past used chlorofluorocarbons because they have low reactivity and are non-poisonous. Nitrogen oxides produced by aircraft burning fossil fuels go into the air and react with the ozone.

Ozone (O_3) is a poisonous gas. However, the layer of ozone in the stratosphere protects the Earth from much of the sun's harmful ultraviolet radiation. The hole in the layer has led to more cases of skin cancer in southern countries such as Australia.

The greenhouse effect

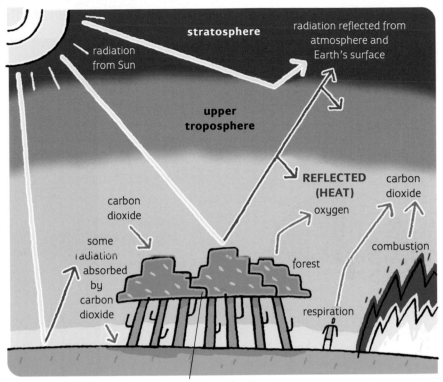

Photosynthesis takes in carbon dioxide
and releases oxygen into the air

The greenhouse effect.

Over the past 200 years the amount of carbon dioxide in the atmosphere has increased by 25%. The carbon dioxide acts like the glass of a greenhouse because it allows heat from the sun to radiate in to the Earth's surface. The heat is then trapped under the stratosphere. The effect is a raising of temperature. This could cause climate changes. As the climate changes so tropical diseases, like malaria and dengue fever will spread northwards.

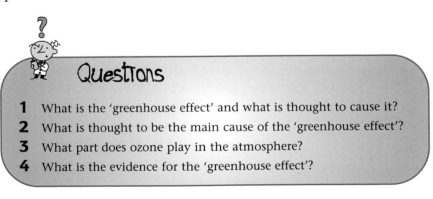

Questions

1 What is the 'greenhouse effect' and what is thought to cause it?
2 What is thought to be the main cause of the 'greenhouse effect'?
3 What part does ozone play in the atmosphere?
4 What is the evidence for the 'greenhouse effect'?

The atmosphere now

The atmosphere

The Earth is surrounded by a layer of gases called the **atmosphere** - largely unchanged for 200 million years. The atmosphere gets less dense as you travel further from the surface.

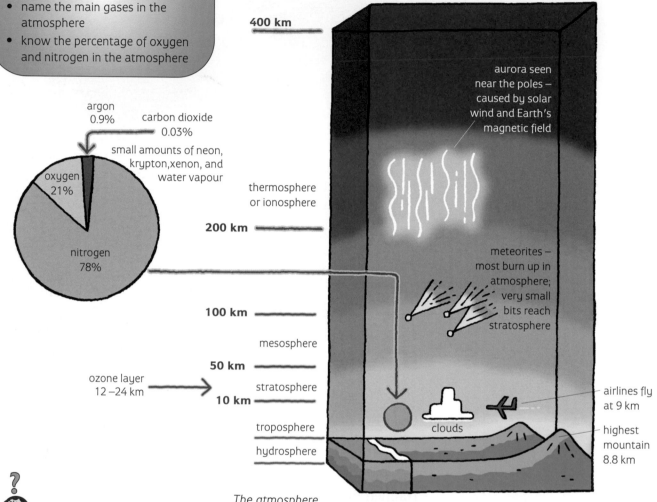

The atmosphere.

The lowest layer of the atmosphere is the layer of air in which we live. It is called the **troposphere**. It is in this layer that weather occurs. **Weather** is the result of movement in the air brought about by shifting blocks of hot and cold air creating winds.

Above the troposphere is the **stratosphere**. The stratosphere contains ozone which absorbs most of the sun's ultraviolet radiation.

Questions

1. Draw a picture of the different layers of the atmosphere.
2. Draw a column graph of the gases in the atmosphere.
3. What does the atmosphere do and why is it important to life on Earth?

The atmosphere is a barrier, protecting the Earth from rocks (meteorites burn up as they pass through it) and radiation. It helps to recycle warmth, water, and chemicals. It is part of a huge chemical factory.

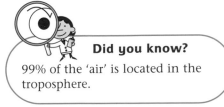
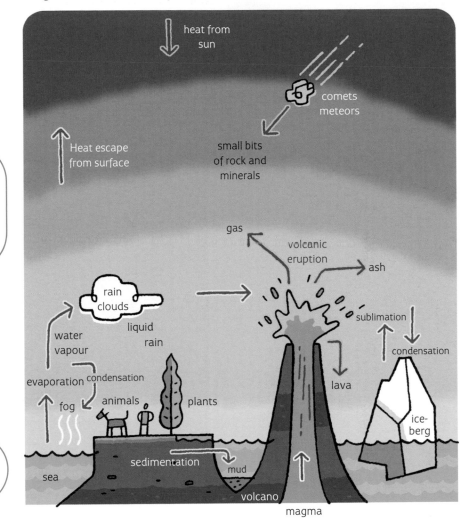

Chemical factory Earth.

The diagram gives some idea of the complicated series of processes that take place in, on, and above the Earth.

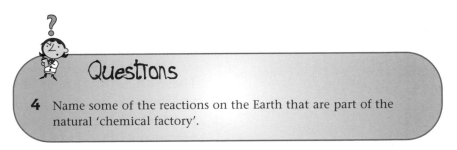

Questions

4 Name some of the reactions on the Earth that are part of the natural 'chemical factory'.

Primitive atmospheres

In the beginning …

Many millions of years ago the Earth was a volcanic wilderness. The oceans were rich in minerals and salts. The atmosphere contained carbon dioxide, carbon monoxide, steam, methane, and ammonia. Any oxygen was bonded in silicates and carbonates, with only very small amounts in the air.

The early Earth.

The Earth's surface cooled and the igneous rocks formed. Volcanoes continued to erupt and the oceans became a 'soup' of minerals and chemicals. Lightning changed ammonia, methane, and carbon monoxide into amino acids. In the warmth of the sea these amino acids formed chains called proteins. Over time other compounds such as DNA were formed in the sea. These proteins and DNA molecules formed small living organisms.

These organisms (one-celled) were primitive bacteria. The DNA attached to the cell wall and inside the cell was a thick liquid in which chemical reactions occurred. Today we can find living organisms like these bacteria living around deep-sea volcanic vents and in the sulphurous pools around volcanoes. Traces of these bacteria are found in rocks about 3.5 billion years old.

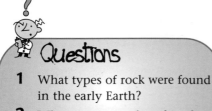

Questions

1 What types of rock were found in the early Earth?

2 What gases were found in the early atmosphere on Earth?

... as time goes on ...

Natural recycling.

Over millions of years these bacteria evolved. They formed a pigment that used light to join carbon dioxide and water into sugars. This reaction released oxygen into the air. As more of these organisms evolved they developed **chlorophyll**. This is the green compound found in plants today. It absorbs energy from sunlight for **photosynthesis** and releases oxygen. Other bacteria organized the inside of the cell to create a nucleus, inside which the DNA was found. These became plant cells.

... and on, and on ...

Plants can live in a carbon dioxide atmosphere. Some of the carbon dioxide in the atmosphere dissolved in the sea, so sea plants could photosynthesize. Photosynthesis changed the atmosphere by adding oxygen. Lightning caused reactions between methane and ammonia, with some of the oxygen made by plants. It left the nitrogen in the air. Some bacteria used the ammonia to make nitrates.

As more oxygen was made, many of the early types of bacteria were killed. In the atmosphere more of the oxygen was changed into ozone (O_3) which blocked harmful radiation from the sun.

The Earth could now evolve more complicated life forms. Animals in the sea used dissolved carbon dioxide to make themselves calcium carbonate shells. This allowed carbon to be recycled from minerals to living things and back to the rocks (including fossil fuels).

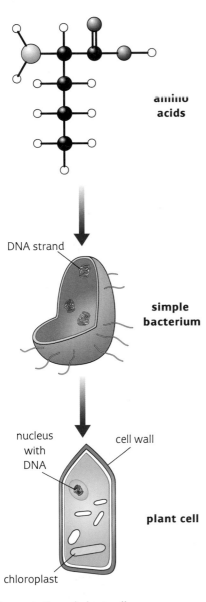

amino acids

DNA strand

simple bacterium

nucleus with DNA

cell wall

plant cell

chloroplast

The evolution of plant cells.

The living Earth

Objectives

This spread should help you to

- describe the Earth's inner structure
- understand the concept of density and the variable density of the Earth

Earthquake damage.

The photograph above shows the damage done by an earthquake. Earthquakes are caused by sudden rock movements underground. The vibrations send **seismic waves** (shockwaves) through the Earth.

Seismic waves get weaker as they travel through the ground. However, many thousands of kilometres away, they can be detected and recorded by a sensitive instrument called a **seismograph**. A simple type is shown below. Any small vibrations in the ground are magnified so that a pen moves up and down. The pen draws a graph on a slowly revolving drum.

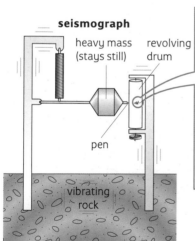

seismograph

heavy mass (stays still)   revolving drum

pen

vibrating rock

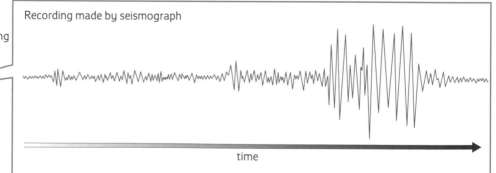

Recording made by seismograph

time

Clues from underground

By studying graphs from recording stations in different places, scientists can work out where the earthquake was, how strong it was, and what kinds of rock the seismic waves travelled through.

Geologists working for oil companies sometimes use small explosions to send shockwaves into the ground. By detecting the waves reflected from different rock layers, they can work out whether there is likely to be any oil in the rocks.

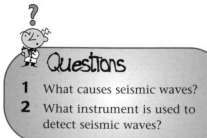

Questions

1 What causes seismic waves?
2 What instrument is used to detect seismic waves?

Inside the Earth

By studying seismic waves, scientists have built up a picture of what the Earth is like inside. There are three main zones:

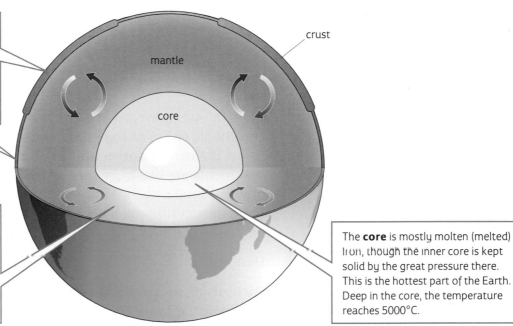

The **crust** is the Earth's thin outer layer. The continents are the thickest part (up to 90 km). The rock here is mainly **granite**. Under the oceans, the crust is thinner and mainly **basalt**.

The **mantle** is mostly solid rock, made of **silicates**. However, the heat and pressure keep it flexible, rather like Plasticine. This means that it can flow. Heat from deep in the Earth makes it circulate very slowly.

The **core** is mostly molten (melted) iron, though the inner core is kept solid by the great pressure there. This is the hottest part of the Earth. Deep in the core, the temperature reaches 5000°C.

Density of the Earth

At the Earth's surface, the rocks have an average density of 2800 kg/m³. In other words, they have 2800 kilograms of mass packed into every cubic metre. However, from the strength of the Earth's gravity, scientists know that the average density of the *whole* Earth must be much higher: 5500 kg/m³.

If rocks at the surface are *less* dense than the average for the whole Earth, then the materials deep in the Earth must be *more* dense. That is one of the reasons why scientists think that the Earth's core is mainly iron.

Questions

3 The diagram on the right shows a simplified section through the Earth. Which of the zones, **X**, **Y**, or **Z**, goes with each of the following?

a the core

b the crust

c the mantle

d flexible enough to flow very slowly

e the hottest zone

f mostly molten iron

g made of the least dense materials

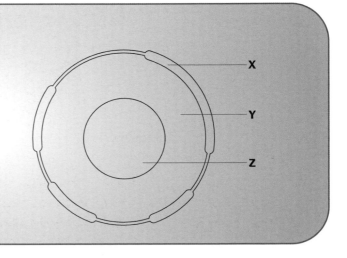

Objectives

This spread should help you to

- give some evidence that the continents are moving
- describe what plates are, and how they are linked with earthquakes

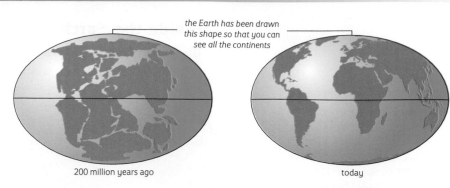

the Earth has been drawn this shape so that you can see all the continents

200 million years ago

today

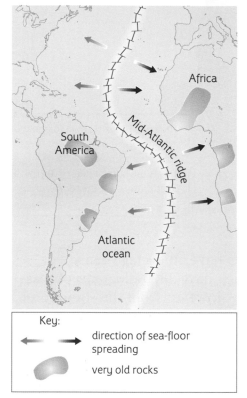

Africa

Mid-Atlantic ridge

South America

Atlantic ocean

Key:

← → direction of sea-floor spreading

very old rocks

In 1915, Alfred Wegener pointed out that the shapes of the continents could fit together like the pieces of a giant jigsaw. In his theory of **continental drift**, he suggested that the continents are like huge rafts which 'float' on the denser material underneath. Millions of years ago, there was one huge supercontinent. This split into pieces, and these have been slowly drifting apart ever since.

Here are two modern pieces of evidence to support this idea:

Patterns of rocks and fossils These match on different continents: for example, along the Atlantic coasts of Africa and South America.

Sea-floor spreading Molten (melted) rock is oozing out of volcanic cracks in a ridge running along the bottom of the Atlantic Ocean. It is cooling, and solidifying to form new crust. As it does so, the Atlantic is slowly getting wider – by a few centimetres a year.

Plates

Scientists now think that the Earth's crust (and upper mantle) is divided up into large sections, called **plates**. These are slowly moving over the denser, more flexible material beneath them. This is **plate tectonics**.

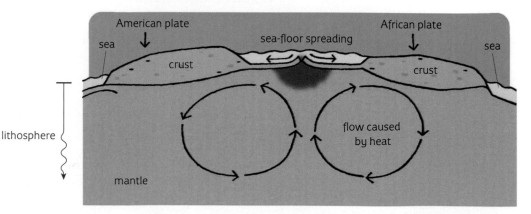

Africa and America are slowly moving apart because of a flow of material in the mantle.

Earthquakes and volcanoes

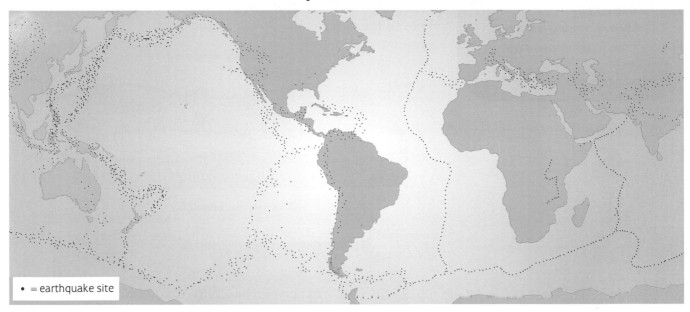

• = earthquake site

Lava flowing from a volcano.

Where plates slide or push against against each other, there may be earthquakes. On the map above, each red dot shows where an earthquake has happened in the last 20 years. Together, the red dots show where the different plates meet.

Most volcanoes are near plate edges, where the crust is cracked and weak. These are also the places where the friction of plates rubbing together can produce heat. Hot rock in the mantle turns liquid and is pushed out from volcanoes as **lava**.

Why plates move

Most of the rock in the mantle is hot but not molten. However, it is flexible enough to flow very slowly, and it does so because of the effect of heat. The heat comes from radioactive materials which are naturally present in the Earth, and it causes **convection currents** in the mantle. (A convection current is a circulating flow of material caused by heat. For example, the hotplate on a cooker causes convection currents in the water in a saucepan.)

Questions

1 In 1915, Alfred Wegener suggested that, millions of years ago, the continents may all have been part of one huge supercontinent. What observation did he make that gave him this idea?

2 Give *two* pieces of evidence to support the idea that the continents have moved apart.

3 What do scientists mean by *plates*?

4 The map at the top of the page shows the sites of earthquakes over the last twenty years.

   a Explain why earthquakes tend to happen along the lines shown, rather than all over the Earth.

   b Explain why volcanoes also tend to be found close to the lines marked by the red dots.

5 What causes the slow movements of the Earth's plates?

Moving continents (2)

Objectives

This spread should help you to

- describe what happens at plate boundaries
- explain how rocks are recycled

The theory of plates and their movements is called **plate tectonics**. Plates meet at boundaries. There are three main types of boundary:

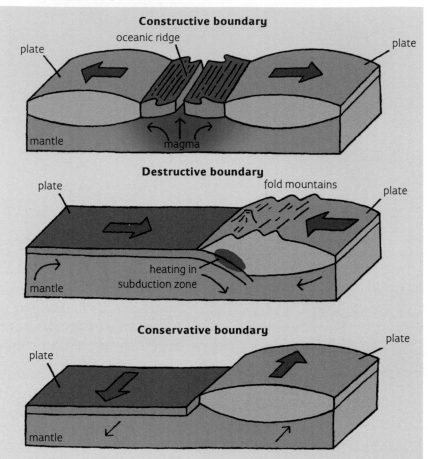

Constructive boundaries These are mainly under oceans. Plates move apart and grow as molten rock oozes up through cracks and cools to form new crust. The molten rock is called **magma**.

Destructive boundaries Plates move together so that one is **subducted** (carried down) under the other. Heat from the friction may melt the rock, causing volcanoes where magma is pushed out of the ground as lava. And as the plates collide, layers of rock are crumpled into **folds**, forming mountains.

Conservative boundaries Plates slide past each other, so their shape is 'conserved' – it does not change. Sometimes, the plates catch on each other. When they jerk free, there may be big earthquakes.

New rocks from old

Over millions of years, rocks in the crust can be subducted, melt to form magma, be uplifted, and then solidify to form new rock. The recycling of old rock to form new is the rock cycle.

Folded rocks.

Rock crystals magnified

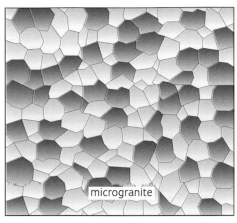

microgranite

This rock cooled more quickly...

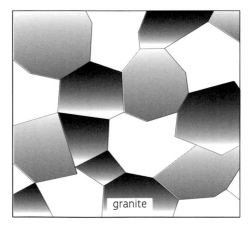

granite

...than this rock.

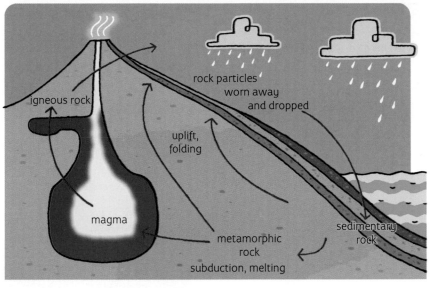

igneous rock

rock particles
worn away
and dropped

uplift,
folding

magma

metamorphic
rock

sedimentary
rock

subduction, melting

There are three main types of rock in the Earth's crust:

Igneous rocks, such as granite and basalt, are made of tiny crystals. They are formed when magma cools and solidifies.

If magma cools *quickly*, the crystals are *small*. This happens, for example, when lava comes out of a volcano and cools. If magma cools *slowly*, the crystals have time to grow, and are *large*. This can happens to magma deep in the crust.

Sedimentary rocks, such as sandstone and limestone, are formed from layers of sediment dropped by water or wind. In many cases, the sediment is bits worn away from old rock. As more sediment collects above it, it gets compressed, and sets like concrete.

Metamorphic rocks Deep underground, igneous and sedimentary rocks can be recrystallized by heat or pressure or both. They become metamorphic ('changed') rock which is usually harder than the original. Examples include marble and slate.

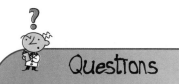

Questions

1 What is *magma*?

2 Here are two ways in which plates may move:

towards each other   *away from each other*

a Which of the above produces fold mountains?

b Which of the above produces a subduction zone?

c In what other way can plates move?

3 Why may volcanoes form above a subduction zone?

4 Why are metamorphic rocks likely to be found near a subduction zone?

5 Igneous rock is formed when magma cools. How could you tell, by looking at the rock, whether the magma had cooled quickly or slowly?

Earth: the big rock cooking pot

Objectives

This spread should help you to
- describe the rock cycle
- describe how rocks form from crystallization reactions

The rock cycle

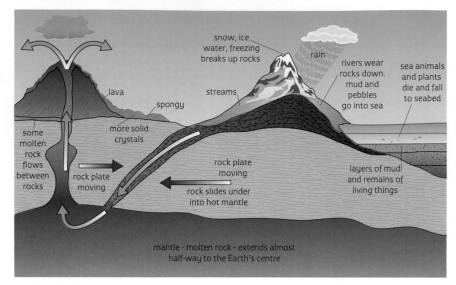

The rock cycle.

The thin surface layer (**crust**) of the earth is made up of several large 'plates'. The plates are always moving, very slowly. When two plates of rock crash into each other, one plate goes beneath the other. The rubbing of the rocks against each other makes a terrific amount of heat – so much that the rocks melt. The rocks go into the very hot **mantle** to form a syrupy liquid. This liquid is under pressure and can escape through volcanoes. Volcanoes can throw out fire, ash, lumps of rock, and rivers of molten rock.

The molten rock (**lava**) flows down the sides of the volcano. As the top surface bubbles with gases, it cools very quickly. It becomes a rock called **pumice**, which looks like the honeycomb centre of a Crunchie bar. Hard, brittle, and full of holes because of the gases, honeycomb and pumice are formed in the same way.

Honeycomb and pumice form in a similar way.

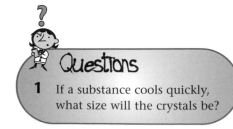

Questions

1 If a substance cools quickly, what size will the crystals be?

When toffee is made, the sugar can crystallize out. Toffee that is cooled very quickly is hard, brittle, and shatters when hit. If rock is cooled so fast that no crystals are made, then **obsidian** is formed. Obsidian is a natural glass.

Rate of cooling	Crystal size	Sweet	Rock
Very fast	Non-crystaline	Very hard toffee	Obsidian
Fast	Very small crystals	Soft toffee	Quick cooling basalt
Slow	Large crystals	Fudge	Slow cooling granite

The rate of cooling affects crystal size in sweets and rocks.

Crystals form round the edges of a geode.

Igneous rocks are mixtures of minerals and these form crystals when the molten rock cools. If the crystals are small because the liquid was cooled quickly, a **basalt** is formed.

When the mineral mixture cools slowly, inside the earth, large crystals form. **Granite** rocks are formed in this way.

Bubbles of liquid can form in the rocks. These solutions of minerals cool slowly and crystals form. This is like a chocolate liqueur sweet filled with sugar solution in which sugar crystals form. In rocks, crystals of many colours can be formed due to the presence of iron or other metals.

Questions

2 What type of rock is formed when molten magma cools very quickly?

3 What is obsidian?

4 Describe how large crystals can be formed from a molten rock.

More on igneous rock

A lava lamp.

If the magma cools in columns it can form structures like the Giants Causeway or those found in Hong Kong.

Questions

1 Name an igneous rock.

Igneous rocks and how they are formed

Igneous comes from the Latin word for 'fire'. Igneous rocks are formed by heat deep inside the Earth.

In lava lamps the wax 'blobs' are heated by the bulb and move up until they cool and then sink. Inside the Earth 'blobs' of molten rock move around in much the same way. **Convection currents** keep the molten rock on the move. This movement helps the Earth to keep its temperature constant. The molten rock is called **magma**.

At weak points in the Earth's surface, such as where two rock plates meet, the liquid rock can come to the surface.

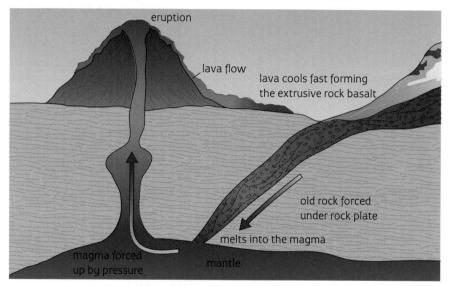

Liquid rock erupts through the Earth's crust in a volcano.

Hot 'magma' flows out of volcanoes on to the surface as lava. This can cool quickly to form basalt rock. Because the lava has been pushed out through the surface (extruded), basalt is called an **extrusive rock**.

As the rock flows over the surface it cools quickly with tiny gas bubbles to become pumice. The crystals formed are very small. Mixed in with the crystals are small pieces of natural glass-like bits. This black, hard, shiny material, obsidian, has hardened without forming crystals.

Some magma flows into cracks and faults in the surrounding rocks, where it cools very slowly. It forms large crystals. The different minerals crystallize out with different colours and the mineral crystals fuse together into a rock.

Granite.

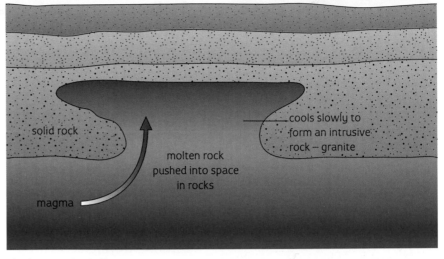

An igneous intrusion.

The rock magma has intruded into the surrounding rock and filled a space so it is called an **intrusive rock**. Granite is an intrusive rock.

The slower the cooling, the larger the crystals as these two types of rock from Sweden show:

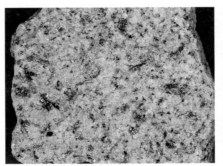

Swedish microgranite has small white crystals.

Swedish porphyrite has large pink crystals

Igneous rocks are formed by processes that involve melting rocks and crystallization at different rates.

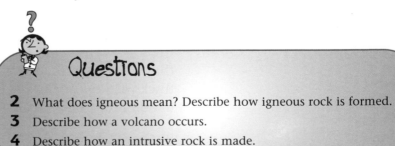

Questions

2 What does igneous mean? Describe how igneous rock is formed.

3 Describe how a volcano occurs.

4 Describe how an intrusive rock is made.

More on sedimentary rock

Objectives

This spread should help you to

• know what sedimentary means

• describe some sedimentary rocks and how they were formed

• know why they are different from each other

Sedimentary rock – our ancestors' story

A sediment is fine particles of solid that settle at the bottom of a liquid. **Sedimentary rocks** were made from bits of other rocks or the hard shells of marine plants and animals.

Over 400 million years ago the area shown below was covered by sea. In the sea were many tiny plants called coccoliths. These had shells of calcium carbonate. When the tiny coccoliths died they sank to the sea floor and decayed, forming a layer of calcium carbonate particles. As more layers built up, the pressure squashed the particles closer together. Some calcium carbonate dissolved in the warm water and as the layers were squashed closer, the particles of calcium carbonate were cemented together to form **chalk**.

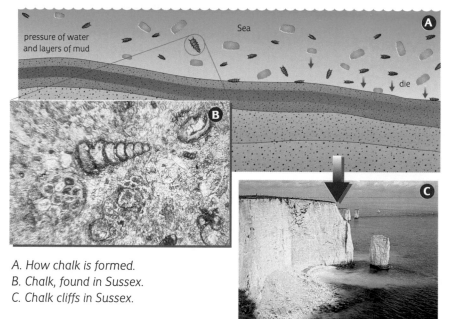

A. How chalk is formed.
B. Chalk, found in Sussex.
C. Chalk cliffs in Sussex.

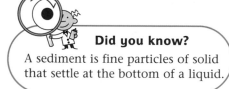

Did you know?

A sediment is fine particles of solid that settle at the bottom of a liquid.

Later, movement of the plates of rock that form the crust of the Earth pushed the rocks up to make the chalk downs of Sussex. For early Britons this land was good. The chalk made the soil alkaline and plants grew well. The rain seeped through the rock and formed springs, making the valleys boggy and thick with trees. Trees like ash were used for weapons and handles for tools. Elder and clematis were good for burning.

In the ancient seas were sea sponges. When they died, they sank to the seabed where their silica skeletons built up in layers. The silica later dissolved and then recrystallized as **flint**. Our ancestors used this flint for building and making tools.

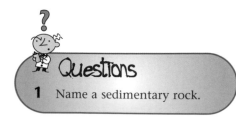

Questions

1 Name a sedimentary rock.

Millstone grit – the climber's tale

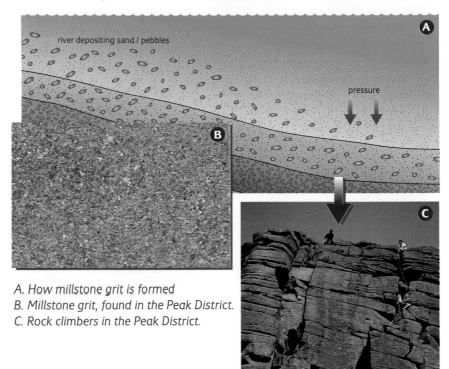

A. How millstone grit is formed
B. Millstone grit, found in the Peak District.
C. Rock climbers in the Peak District.

Climbers choose their rocks very carefully. One big favourite is **millstone grit**. This is because it is coarse, with many crevices and cracks. It makes an excellent climbing surface.

Millions of years ago, huge rivers flowing over rocks carried away small pieces of rock. Where the river flowed more slowly, the particles settled out in layers. Chemicals dissolved in the water also precipitated out and cemented the particles together into layers of rock. These layers are a mixture of hard and soft rock. Over the centuries the soft rock has been worn away, forming ledges and crevices that are good for climbing.

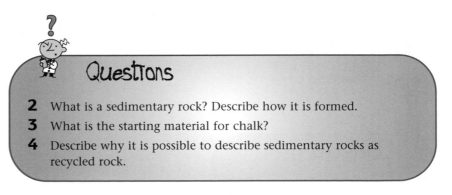

Questions

2 What is a sedimentary rock? Describe how it is formed.

3 What is the starting material for chalk?

4 Describe why it is possible to describe sedimentary rocks as recycled rock.

More on metamorphic rock

Objectives

This spread should help you to

- know what metamorphic means
- describe some metamorphic rocks, how they were formed, and that they are involved in tectonic processes.
- know why they are different

Metamorphic rock

Turning clay on a wheel to shape it and then placing it in a hot kiln is a form of **metamorphosis**. Metamorphosis means transformation Metamorphic rocks are involved in **plate tectonics.**

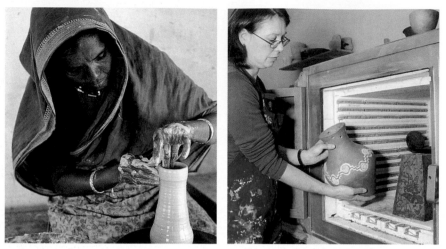

A. Wet, soft clay.   B. Hard, solid, dry pot.

Just as the clay is changed by the heat in the kiln, so rocks are changed by the great heat inside the Earth. It is not just the heat in the Earth that changes the rock. The great weight of rock above puts pressure on rocks deep in the Earth.

Mud under pressure forms a rock called **shale**. Shale can be metamorphosed into **slate** by high temperature and pressure.

At even higher temperature and pressure the minerals in the slate change to different minerals and form the rock **schist**. This rock is shiny and has wavy folds.

Metamorphosis: ...mud   ...shale...   ...slate...   ...schist...

From limestone to marble

Limestone is a sedimentary rock but it can be changed by high temperatures and pressure into marble.

Limestone is calcium carbonate. When it is compressed at high temperature, the crystals reform into bigger, closely locked crystals. If there are other minerals in the marble then the marble is coloured.

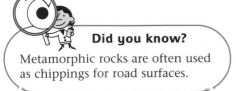

Did you know?
Metamorphic rocks are often used as chippings for road surfaces.

Limestone: rough texture.

Marble: gives a fine texture. Michaelangelo's 'David' is carved from marble.

Marble can have many different colours.

When the crystals reform closer together in marble it makes the rock harder. Rocks that have been changed and become metamorphic rocks are harder. When granite is changed it forms the harder rock **gneiss**.

Questions

2 What is a metamorphic rock? Describe how it is formed.

3 What rock is the starting material for marble?

4 What makes a rock change and describe what 1 happens to the crystals.

Weathering and erosion

The effect of water

The water cycle.

The sun's heat evaporates water from the sea and other water surfaces. Moist air rises into the atmosphere. As the air cools the water vapour condenses into small drops and forms clouds. Eventually the water droplets fall as rain. The rain water flows off the land as rivers or soaks into rocks like chalk. The water passes down to igneous rock. It cannot soak into layers of igneous rock so it flows over the rock to come out elsewhere as a spring.

Some water is taken up by plants. It is drawn up from the roots to the leaves and evaporates through tiny holes in the leaves (transpiration). Some water is taken up by animals and passed out as waste.

The processes

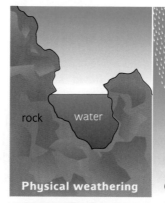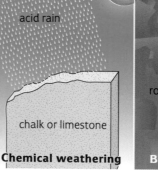

Physical weathering

Water collects in crevices. It freezes and expands. As this happens many times, the rock cracks and breaks off.

Chemical weathering

Rain dissolves acid gases from the air. This water collects in pools. The sun heats the water, concentrates the solution. Acid rain reacts with the carbonate rock.

Biological weathering

Plants grow in cracks. Their roots push down between the rocks, forcing them apart.

Weathering is the process of breaking up rocks. The rock bits are carried along, or transported, by flowing water. As the water flows it wears away the rock because of the tiny bits of rock rubbing on other rocks. Chemical reactions also wear down rocks.

Wind can also wear down rocks. Tiny bits of sand blown in the air blast away at soft rock, wearing away the surface.

Erosion is the carrying away of bits of rock.

Weathering acting on faults

Water weathering and erosion.

Wind weathering and erosion of rock by sand

Weathering and erosion by water flow

Questions

3 What is weathering? Describe how it works to form sand and soil.

4 What is the difference between weathering and erosion?

Practice questions

1 Give two reasons why the percentage of carbon dioxide in the atmosphere is increasing.

2 Write two paragraphs, one on recycling of waste materials and one on landfill sites, using the words:

**bottle banks   paper   glass   textiles
percentage of waste recycled**

and

**90% household rubbish   biodegradable
non-bidegradable   methane gas
polluted liquid**

3 Write out the following three sentences, choosing the correct words from the list supplied:

'Igneous rocks such as _____ and _____ are often composed of _____.'

'_____ rocks such as limestone and _____ often contain _____.'

'_____ rocks such as _____ and _____ are often hard and shiny.'

Word list:

**metamorphic   basalt   fossils   shale
granite   sedimentary   marble
differently coloured crystals   slate**

4 Igneous (fiery) rocks are made from molten material.

a Give the name of the molten material and explain where it comes from.

b Describe what happens to the molten material when it becomes:

i intrusive rock

ii extrusive rock

iii pumice.

5 Write a paragraph explaining how sedimentary rocks are formed using the terms: erosion (wearing down), transportation (carrying away), deposition (settling), cementation (sticking together).

6 Write out the following passage choosing the correct word from the selection in the brackets to fill in the spaces:

'Some buildings, like the Houses of Parliament, are made of _____ (**sandstone/brick/limestone**) and are wearing away because the stone is full of _____ (**dirt particles/large shells**) which break up and fall out leaving _____ (**cavities/particles/cracks**). These allow water to get in and when it _____ (**heats up/freezes**) the stone _____ (**dissolves/cracks**) and layers _____ (**peel off/disappear**).'

7 a How is metamorphic rock formed?

b Explain how slate and schist are made from mud.

8 The diagram below shows the rock cycle. Copy and complete the diagram by filling in the boxes, using the labels provided:

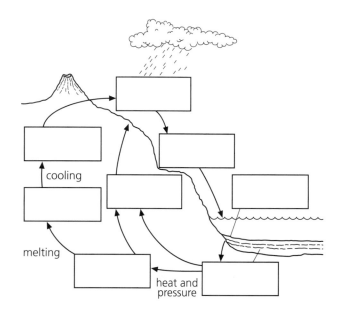

Labels for boxes

igneous rocks   erosion and transport   weathering
sedimentary rocks   deposition   magma
metamorphic rocks   uplift and folding

9 Copy and complete the sentences using words from the list provided.

'Granite is very _____ and is used for _____ and _____.

Marble is a _____ form of limestone and is used for _____ and _____.

Slate splits into _____ sheets and is used for _____ and _____.'

Word list:

**snooker tables   metamorphic   hard
building stone   statues   roofing
decorative chippings   flat   gravestones**

10 a What are fossil fuels?

b How were they formed?

c What are the two main elements in all fossil fuels?

d What other elements are often present?

11 Copy and complete the flow chart showing how limestone is converted to mortar, cement, and concrete, filling in the boxes with words from the following list:

quicklime   sand   clay   water   slaked lime   chippings

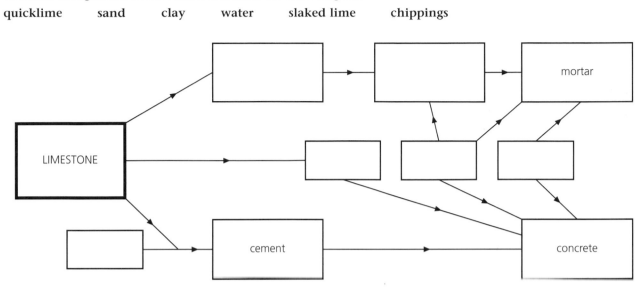

12 a Explain what is meant by the fractional distillation of crude oil?

b Are longer chain hydrocarbons more or less volatile and viscous than shorter chain hydrocarbons?

c Describe the process of cracking oil fractions.

d What are the kinds of molecules produced by cracking?

13 Copy the table and rearrange the layers of the atmosphere, their heights and features into the correct order, starting with the lowest.

Layer	Height (km)	Feature
meosphere	10	weather occurs
stratosphere	50	mainly changed particles
ionosphere	80	contains ozone layer
troposphere	400	meteorites burn up

14 a Name and give the percentages of the gases in the atmosphere.

b Name the gases present originally in the atmosphere when the Earth first formed.

15 Explain:

a how primitive living organisms were formed from the gases in the Earth's original atmosphere

b how oxygen gas came to be released into the atmosphere.

16 Describe the causes and effects of:

a physical weathering

b chemical weathering

c erosion.

17 a What are the fossil fuels?

b What are the four main elements in fossil fuels?

c What are the gases formed when fossil fuels are burned?

d How can coal be cleaned to avoid producing harmful gases when it is burned?

27 Write out the following table and put ticks in the appropriate spaces to show whether the processes listed would increase, decrease, or have no effect on the amount of carbon dioxide in the atmosphere.

Process	Amount of carbon dioxide		
	Increase	Decrease	No effect
Burning carbon			
Photosynthesis			
Transpiration			
Burning magnesium			
Respiration			
Raining			
Burning fuel oil			
Perspiring			

Key words

acid rain when a gas like sulphur dioxide, nitrogen oxide, carbon dioxide dissolves in rain the pH ions forming an acid

anticlines a dome shaped rock structure

atmosphere layer of gas surrounding the Earth

bacteria – denitrifying, nitrifying, putrefying single celled organisms which release or fix nitrogen

basalt an igneous rock with small crystals of minerals generally found when molten rock pushes out on the surface – extrusive rock

bio-degradable material that breaks down in the environment harmlessly

chalk a sedimentary rock formed from tiny plants

chlorophyll a green pigment chemical found in plants that catalysis photosynthesis

coal a fossil fuel

conglomerate a mixture of rocks naturally cemented together with calcium carbonate

cracking when a large alkane molecule is broken into small molecules

density the mass of a substance divided by the volume
$$D = \frac{M}{V} \ (D = M \div V)$$

erosion the wearing down of rocks by wind or water

flint a sedimentary rock formed from recrystallised silica of sponges

folded rocks rock layers 'bent' by the Earth's surface movements

fossil fuels a fuel formed from partially rotted animals and plants many millions of years old

fractional distillation where a liquid mixture is heated and boiled and the different parts condensed and removed

granite a hard igneous rock with large crystals of minerals generally formed when molten rock pushes into a space or crystallises – intrusive rock

hydrocarbons a compound made of carbon and hydrogen

igneous rocks rocks formed from molten magma and full of minerals

lava molten rock coming out of a volcano

lithosphere the crust and the top part of the mantle

meta-morphic rocks rocks produced in Earth's surface by the pressures of heat and pressure

magma molten rock

meta-morphosis a rock that is changed into another due to heat/pressure

minerals solid element or naturally occurring compound

monomers small molecules with a double bond that is broken to link them into a long chain

obsidian igneous rocks cooled so fast there are no crystals – glass like

ores a mineral or rock containing metals that can be extracted

plate tectonics the process of movement of 'plates' of the Earth's surface

pollution the spreading of unwanted and harmful substances into the environment

90

polymer	a chain of monomers	**thermal decomp- osition**	when a chemical breaks down into simpler compounds with heat
polymer- ization	when simple molecules are chemically joined to form a large chain	**troposphere**	the lower layer of the atmosphere in contact with the crust
potential energy	stored energy	**water cycle**	the cycle by which water evaporates to form clouds and then rain to fall back to the land
pumice	light igneous rock full of air holes		
rock cycle	the process of renewal of the rocky outer surface of the Earth	**weather**	the result of air current movements
rocks	a mixture of minerals found in the Earth's crust	**weathering**	the process of breaking up rocks by physical, chemical or biological means
sedimentary rocks	rocks formed by sediments layering and under pressure forming rocks		
stratosphere	the layer of the atmosphere above the troposphere where much of the ozone is found		

Chemical reactions can be fast or slow. Chemists use the speed of a reaction to produce different things. Explosives work because the reaction is very fast. They can be very useful things to make. Rusting is an example of a slow reaction, which is not so useful.

Particles and reactions

Objectives

This spread should help you to
- describe the collision theory
- write a simple chemical equation
- describe solids, liquids, and gases.

Collisions between particles

Particles cannot react if they are kept apart. To react the particles have to collide. But not all collisions produce a reaction.

A glancing collision.   *A head-on collision.*

If two football players walk towards each other and collide there will be little damage. Very little energy is involved.

If the two football players run very fast and just touch each other, this glancing hit changes the direction of movement, but no reaction takes place because not enough energy is involved.

If the two heavy footballers run directly at each other very fast, a large amount of energy is involved. The energy of the collision makes them react.

Increasing the energy of collision

In a solid the particles cannot move very fast or collide very well. This means few chemical reactions can take place and any that do will take a long time.

In a liquid the particles are able to move quickly and roll over each other and collide with others. Chemical reactions can easily occur in liquids.

In a gas the particles move very fast and often collide with each other. Chemical reactions can easily occur in a gas.

Solid
Particles
vibrate

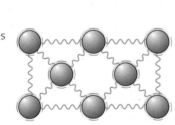

solid + solid: little chance of collisions
solid + liquid: better chance of collisions

Little chance of collision.

Liquid
Particles
vibrate and
roll over
each other

stirring the liquid increases particle movement
heating the liquid increases energy of particles

Many opportunities for collisions.

Gas
Particles
free to move,
lot of
vibration and
translation

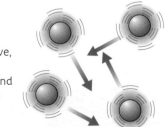

increasing temperature increases
energy of particles

Lots of collisions, some are glancing and some are head on.

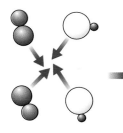

Two different types of particles collide

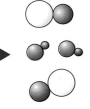

Particles change places and a new type of particle is formed

compound A
+
compound B

$\longrightarrow$

compound C
+
compound D

Particles collide and react.

Particles have changed places.

When atoms or molecules collide it is not the nuclei that hit each other. It is the outer electrons that collide and react. Sometimes they form bonds. Sometimes a bond between two particles is broken and reforms between different particles. This makes a new substance.

Conservation of matter

When reactions take place between substances it is possible to see that the number of atoms remains the same. But the way they are joined together is different.

So why do the substances in some reactions appear to lose mass?

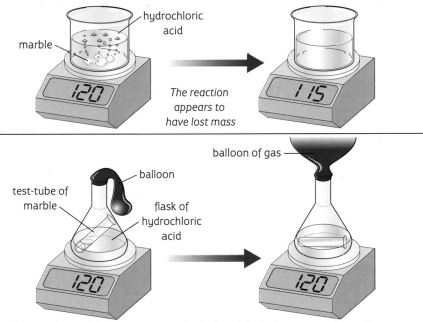

hydrochloric acid

marble

120

The reaction appears to have lost mass

115

balloon of gas

balloon

test-tube of marble

flask of hydrochloric acid

120

120

All the products of the reaction are in the flask and the balloon, so no change in mass

The reason in this case lies in the bubbles you see. These bubbles are a gas that is made in the reaction. In this reaction the gas is given off very fast. In some reactions it happens very slowly. If you weigh the equipment as the reaction is taking place, you can measure the volume or mass of gas given off over time. This tells you how fast the reaction is going.

Questions

1 What must particles do if they are to react?

2 What are the best states for chemical reactions to happen in?

3 What particle in the atom is involved in a chemical reaction?

4 Why do some reactions seem to lose mass?

Rates of reaction

What is a rate of reaction?

Imagine two teams of men painting a wall. They are competing to see who can finish the quickest. One team is fit with plenty of energy. The other is not so fit and has less energy. At the end of the competition the fit team has painted twice as much as the unfit team.

The rate of the fit team is 2× faster than the unfit team. If the wall was 8 metres in length, the rate of painting would be:

$$\frac{8 \text{ metres}}{4 \text{ hours}} = 2 \text{ metres per hour}$$

The unfit team's rate is 4 metres in 4 hours:

$$\frac{4 \text{ metres}}{4 \text{ hours}} = 1 \text{ metre per hour}$$

Chemical reactions also work at different rates.

Very slow chemical reaction – limestone reacts very slowly with rainwater to form these stalactites.

Fast chemical reaction – oxygen reacts with the chemicals in the plants.

Very rapid chemical reaction – lots of gas, lots of heat, very quickly.

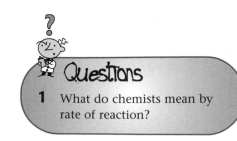

Questions

1 What do chemists mean by rate of reaction?

To the chemist:

Rate is a measure of the change taking place in a single unit of time such as a second or minute.

Measuring rates of change

To measure change it is important to measure two things: time and the amount of change. That change can be:

- the mass of gas produced
- the mass of solid produced
- the change in colour
- the loss in mass of a solid

You can measure the change at regular time intervals. To draw a graph of this, plot time on the x or bottom axis. The shape of the graph line tells you if the rate is fast or slow.

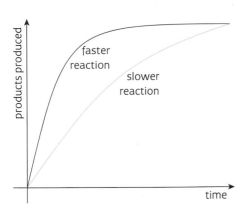

Fast and slow rates of change

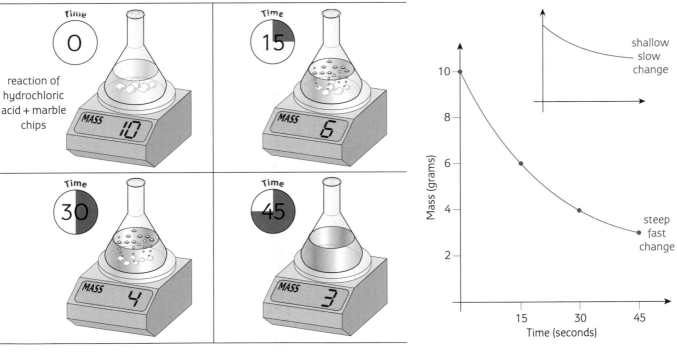

The reaction of hydrochloric acid and marble.

Reaction rates can be controlled by changing the temperature, the concentration of reactants, the size of reactant particles, or by using catalysts.

Questions

2 Describe a fast reaction and a slow reaction.

3 What can you measure to work out the rate of reaction?

4 How can you change the rate of reaction?

5 In industry, why might 'rate of reaction' be important

Objectives

This spread should help you to

- describe rate of reaction
- describe how concentration, surface area, and pressure affect the rate of reaction
- show how, on a graph, rate of reaction varies with concentration and surface area

How concentration changes the rate of reaction

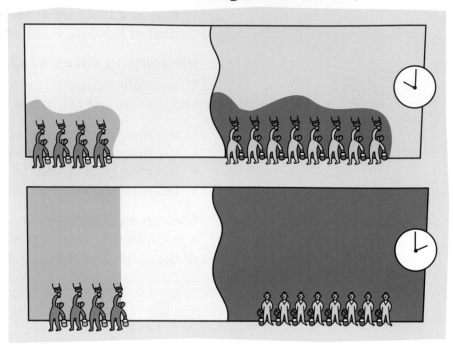

Imagine painters painting a wall. With four men painting there are four paintbrushes putting paint on the wall. While with eight men in the team, there are eight paintbrushes – twice as many brushes making contact with the wall. The concentration of painters is greater with eight men and so the wall is painted faster.

In this model of a reaction, the men and their paintbrushes represent the particles. The contact of the paintbrush with the wall is the collision of the particles. The more particles, the more collisions and the more reactions can take place.

Pressure

Increased pressure increases the 'concentration' of collisions so increases the rate of reaction.

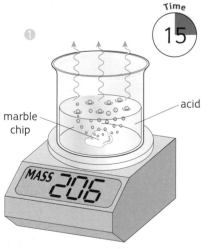

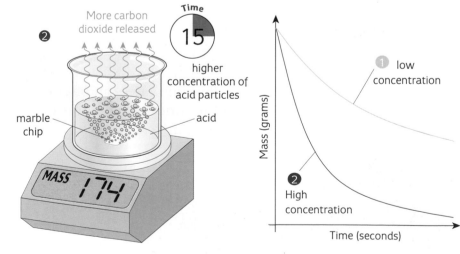

The more particles, the more collisions.

How surface area changes the rate of reaction

Small, thin chips fry faster than big fat ones.

A tablet broken into pieces dissolves faster than a whole tablet.

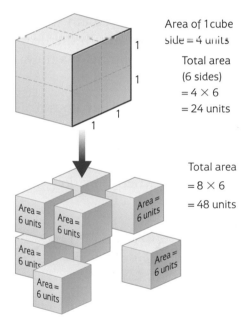

Area of 1 cube
side = 4 units

Total area
(6 sides)
= 4 × 6
= 24 units

Total area
= 8 × 6
= 48 units

Area =
6 units

More pieces: bigger surface area.

In everyday life people often make things smaller to make them react faster. Why does this work?

If you put a piece of a solid in a liquid, only the outside surfaces of the solid can react. If you break it into smaller pieces, it has more surface area. Imagine dissolving a jelly cube in hot water. You can put it in hot water as a whole block or broken up into smaller pieces. The smaller the size of each piece the larger the total surface area.

When a solid is broken down into smaller pieces, more particles are exposed and can collide. More reactions can take place and so the rate of reaction will increase.

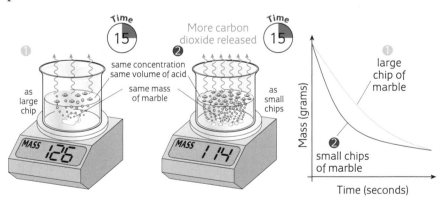

Small chips of marble react faster than one big lump of marble.

Questions

1 How does surface area affect rate of reaction?

2 Which will react faster and why: a large lump of calcium carbonate or powdered calcium carbonate?

3 How does concentration affect the rate of reaction?

Changing rates (2)

Objectives

This spread should help you to

- describe rate of reaction
- describe how temperature, pressure, and catalysts affect the rate of reaction
- know that enzymes are biological catalysts
- show how, on a graph, rate of reaction varies with temperature

How temperature affects rate

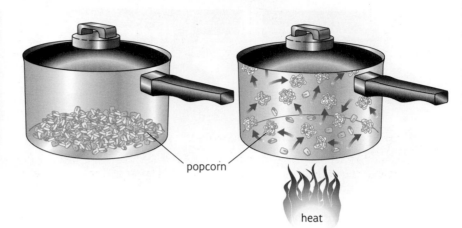

popcorn

heat

Pressure

A higher pressure will increase the 'rate of reaction'.

Smaller space means more collisions and more chance for reaction.

Imagine a saucepan of popcorn. When cold, the pieces of popcorn cover the bottom of the saucepan and remain still. Heat up the saucepan and the popcorn pieces absorb the heat energy and start moving about. They start 'popping'. As they move about they collide a lot.

Particles in a compound react in a similar way. They do not increase in size like popcorn. But they do move about and as the heat increases, they move faster. More collisions occur and so more reactions take place. Increasing the temperature means the particles have more energy. So when they do collide they are more likely to react.

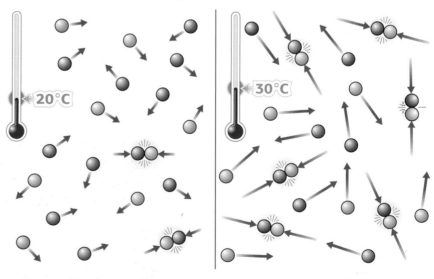

Chemicals reacting at 20°C   *Chemicals reacting at 30°C*

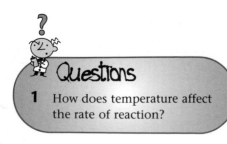

Questions

1 How does temperature affect the rate of reaction?

Not all collisions will lead to a reaction. A glancing collision means the particles slide past but do not have enough energy or come close enough to react. Temperature has a very big effect on the rate of reaction. A rise of 10°C can double the rate.

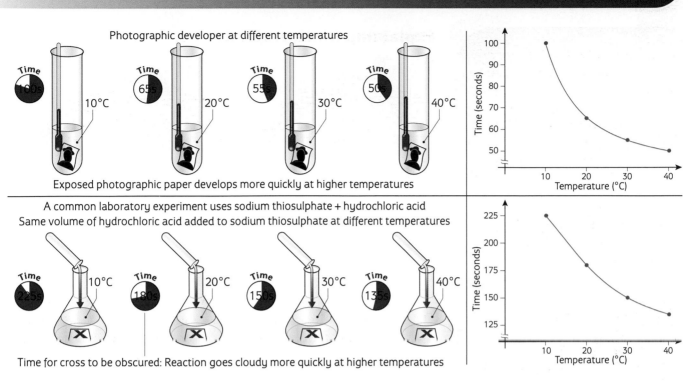

Photographic developer at different temperatures

Time 100s — 10°C
Time 65s — 20°C
Time 55s — 30°C
Time 50s — 40°C

Exposed photographic paper develops more quickly at higher temperatures

A common laboratory experiment uses sodium thiosulphate + hydrochloric acid
Same volume of hydrochloric acid added to sodium thiosulphate at different temperatures

Time 225s — 10°C
Time 180s — 20°C
Time 150s — 30°C
Time 135s — 40°C

Time for cross to be obscured: Reaction goes cloudy more quickly at higher temperatures

Two examples of the effect of temperature on a reaction.

Catalysts in everyday life

Catalysts are materials that are used to help chemical reactions take place more quickly. They are not part of the chemical reaction and remain unchanged. The metal nickel is used as a catalyst in the making of margarine. Iron is used as a catalyst in the production of ammonia. Catalysts always speed up chemical reactions.

An **enzyme** is a biological catalyst. For example, enzymes in your liver speed up the breakdown of hydrogen peroxide.

Other enzymes at work:

• biological detergent (proteases/lipases)
• carbohydrase converts starch into sugar
• isomerase converts glucose into fructose
• protease to 'pre-digest' baby food protein

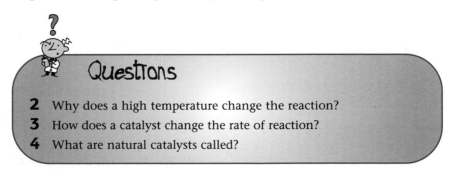

Questions

2 Why does a high temperature change the reaction?

3 How does a catalyst change the rate of reaction?

4 What are natural catalysts called?

Enzymes and biotechnology

This spread should help you to

- know what an enzyme is and what it does
- know some reactions that occur because of enzymes
- describe how enzymes work
- know the test for limewater

Winemaking uses enzymes.

Did you know?
The test for carbon dioxide is limewater – which goes cloudy.

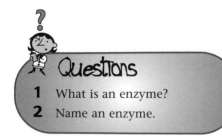

Questions

1 What is an enzyme?
2 Name an enzyme.

Explaining biotechnology

Enzymes are used to make all of these.

What do yoghurt, penicillin, soy sauce, wine, beer, bread, and cheese have in common? They have all been produced by the action of enzymes. They are products of **biotechnology**.

Biotechnology is the use of natural processes for the industrial production of material. Enzymes are involved in many of the processes.

Enzymes

Enzymes are found in all living things. They are biological catalysts. All are proteins. They work by lowering the energy needed to break and make bonds in a chemical reaction and speeding up the reaction. At the end of the reaction they are unchanged.

However, they can be badly affected by high temperature and some chemical conditions such as acidity/alkalinity.

Enzymes in your body

Your mouth produces saliva which contains the enzyme amylase. Teeth reduce food to small pieces. This helps to speed up the reaction by increasing the surface area. The six salivary glands produce the saliva. It helps to lubricate dry food and surround the food with enzyme. Amylase works best at temperatures close to 37 °C and in alkaline conditions near pH 7.5. It breaks down starch into sugars.

Once food gets into the stomach the enzyme pepsin works on it. But pepsin works better at temperatures close to 40 °C and in acid conditions of pH 2.

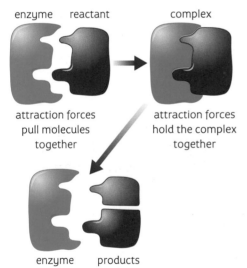

Enzymes are left unchanged at the end of the reaction. The reactant fits the enzyme like a key in a lock.

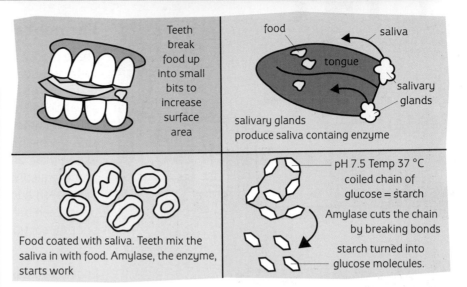

Teeth break food up into small bits to increase surface area

salivary glands produce saliva containg enzyme

Food coated with saliva. Teeth mix the saliva in with food. Amylase, the enzyme, starts work

pH 7.5 Temp 37 °C coiled chain of glucose = starch

Amylase cuts the chain by breaking bonds

starch turned into glucose molecules.

Eating and enzymes.

How enzymes work

An enzyme is a shaped molecule of many atoms. The shape is important because specific areas attract other molecules. These molecules lock in to the enzyme's shape just like jigsaw pieces. This forms a **complex**. In the complex the shape of the reactant molecule is changed. This allows bonds to be broken and new ones formed.

When the enzyme separates from the complex it is unchanged. But the reactant has been changed. Changes in temperature and pH cause the shape of the enzyme to change. This may make it difficult for it to work. Biotechnology makes use of enzymes in fermenters. In a fermenter temperature and pH can be controlled to allow a chemical reaction called fermentation to take place.

The brewing, wine, spirit, and bread industries all use yeast. Yeast is a type of fungus that uses enzymes to break sugar down into ethanol and carbon dioxide. The dairy industry uses bacteria and their enzymes to produce cheese and yoghurt (by converting sugar in milk to lactic acid). Medicines such as insulin are produced by using bacteria.

Questions

3 Name a reaction that works better because of an enzyme.

4 How do enzymes work?

Fermentation

These products all have something in common. They were produced by fermentation. Imagine that the water were so bad as to be undrinkable. This was the situation in England and many countries in Europe in medieval times. To get a drink that was tasty and safe, people made ale. This is a drink made from water, malt, and yeast, which is fermented to produce alcohol. To this they added fruit and spices, some even added the smelly, sticky sap from pine trees. Each brewmaster had his or her own recipe, but the reaction is the same.

In the 16th century, hops were added to ale in England, and beer began to be made. The amount of alcohol produced in an ale or beer is low compared to that in wine and spirits.

Wine has been made for over 10 000 years. It was made by fermenting the sugars in fruit using natural yeast. This yeast is the dull waxy coating on the outside of the fruit. Sometimes they fermented honey using yeast, and this was called mead. The Vikings were great drinkers of mead.

Louis Pasteur

ALCOHOL

Alcohol in drinks kills some of the bacteria in water that cause stomach upsets. However, when the alcohol concentration reaches 15%, it also kills the yeast.

Long ago, people realized that very strong alcohol was good for cleaning wounds. In fact, it is the second oldest disinfectant used by humans. The oldest disinfectant is urine from a 'healthy, clean-living person'.

Louis Pasteur was the first to investigate fermentation scientifically. He found that very cold and very hot conditions stopped fermentation.

Distillation

To make the alcohol concentration higher than 15%, people distilled wine. The Chinese in the 4th century were probably the first to use alcohol. The idea did not travel to Europe until 500 years later. The Chinese found that when wine froze in winter, there was always a liquid left unfrozen. This liquid or 'spirit' was collected and added to wine to fortify it. Distillation by heating the wine and collecting the vapour and cooling it started in China in the 7th century. It was called 'burnt wine' or brandy.

In Scotland and Ireland the distillation of fermented barley and malt produces whisky. In France the distillation of wine produces brandy. The fermented sugar solution contains about 8% alcohol plus many different flavours due to extracts from the original plants. It is heated and the vapours are collected. The more this is repeated, the stronger the alcohol, but the danger is that the flavour could be damaged. The chemist must try to increase the alcohol content of the drink without spoiling the flavour.

Low-alcohol beers

Low-alcohol beers are produced to:

- allow people to drink and drive
- allow people to drink without breaking religious rules

This process for the chemist is the reverse of distillation. After fermentation the alcohol needs to be removed without the flavour being damaged. The liquid is distilled to remove alcohol and then re-blended with flavours so it tastes like a beer. The alcohol content must be very low if you want to drink and still drive safely.

Talking point

Think of some alcoholic drinks. How were they made?

Breadmaking

Bread is made by fermentation. Enzymes in yeast convert the starch in the flour to glucose. Then they ferment the glucose, producing carbon dioxide. The small holes are produced by carbon dioxide gas. It is this gas that makes bread rise and the bread flavour comes from the small amount of alcohol produced and flavours in the cereal. The oven heat kills the yeast, stopping the reaction.

Yeast feeds on the sugar glucose, turning it into alcohol. Glucose is a complex molecule. Enzymes in yeast, like zymase, break down the glucose molecule into ethanol. This releases carbon dioxide.

glucose (aqueous)	enzyme $\longrightarrow$	ethanol (aqueous)	+	carbon dioxide (gas)
$C_6H_{12}O_6(aq)$	zymase $\longrightarrow$	$2C_2H_5OH(aq)$	+	$2CO_2(g)$

Energy changes in reactions

Objectives

This spread should help you to

- describe activation energy
- draw a diagram showing how energy helps a reaction
- know where the energy transfer occurs in a chemical reaction

Moving particles have kinetic energy.

Energy in reactions

A match rubbed quickly along a rough surface bursts into flame.

The friction between the match and the rough surface transfers energy as heat. You feel the same effect when you rub your hands together very fast. This heat energy is transferred to the chemicals in the match head.

The chemical bonds are vibrating but hold together because of attraction between atoms. The atoms have moving energy in the vibrations and stored energy in the attraction. The moving energy is called **kinetic energy** and the stored energy is **potential energy**. It is the kinetic energy that allows chemical reactions to happen.

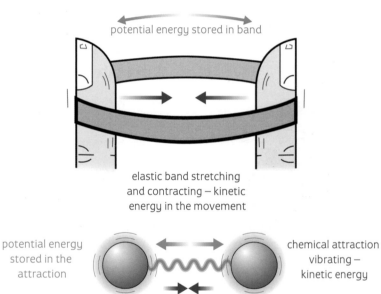

A chemical 'attraction' behaves a bit like a rubber band.

If the vibration is very big, it will stretch the bond so far that it breaks (just as an elastic band will break). This transfers energy as kinetic energy to the particles. They move and collide and have high kinetic energy.

When particles collide reactions happen in which new products are formed.

Activation energy

The amount of energy particles need to be able to react is called the **activation energy**. It can be thought of as the amount of energy given to the elastic band to just break it. Like the elastic band the attraction between the particles resist the breaking. They prefer to bend or vibrate. But eventually like the elastic band the energy is sufficient to break the attraction.

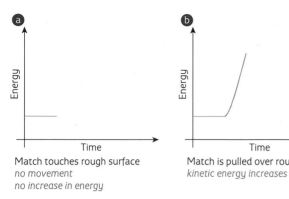

a — Match touches rough surface
no movement
no increase in energy

b — Match is pulled over rough surface
kinetic energy increases

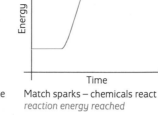

c — Match sparks – chemicals react
reaction energy reached

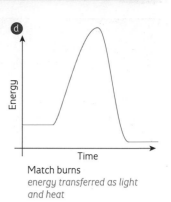

d — Match burns
energy transferred as light and heat

Drawing an energy graph.

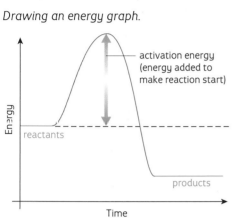

activation energy (energy added to make reaction start)

reactants

products

Energy

Time

The complete energy graph.

You can show this on a diagram. When the match touches the surface and remains still the energy of the chemicals in the match head is low and stays constant. As the match is rubbed along the surface, the movement energy is transferred to the chemicals. This increases the energy of the chemicals until the match sparks. The chemical reaction has started. As the match burns it transfers energy as heat and light and the energy of the chemicals decreases.

Activation energy is the energy transferred to the reactants to make the reaction begin. On the diagram the difference in energy between the reactants line – the starting point – and the top of the hump is the activation energy.

Temperature measures the average kinetic energy of the particles. You can follow the energy changes using a thermometer or a heat sensor on a computer. As the kinetic energy increases, the temperature increases.

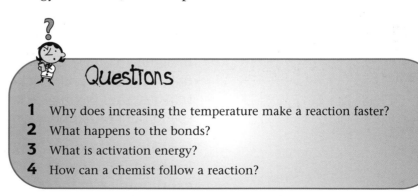

Questions

1 Why does increasing the temperature make a reaction faster?
2 What happens to the bonds?
3 What is activation energy?
4 How can a chemist follow a reaction?

Objectives

This spread should help you to

- know what 'exothermic' means
- describe what happens to the temperature in an exothermic reaction

Exothermic reaction

Railway lines need very careful welding to make them smooth and prevent the constant 'clack-clack'. Railway tracks are made of very hard steel and to join them requires a strong weld.

This is done by using a mixture of aluminium powder and iron(III) oxide. The mixture is heated to make the bonds vibrate to breaking point. At the breaking the aluminium attracts the oxygen away from the iron(II) oxide and forms a new compound – aluminium oxide. The iron atoms are vibrating so much that the metal is in liquid form. The liquid iron runs out of the bottom of the container into the gap between the rails. Here it cools and forms a solid. This welds the rails together.

Using the Thermit reaction to weld railway lines together.

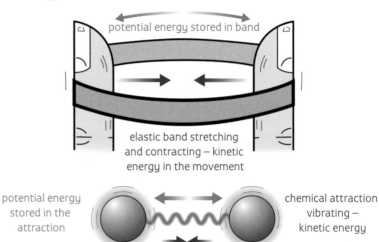

potential energy stored in band

elastic band stretching and contracting – kinetic energy in the movement

potential energy stored in the attraction

chemical attraction vibrating – kinetic energy

Energy: loss or gain?

In this reaction a large amount of energy is transferred to the surroundings. Heat comes out and the container is hot.

Imagine you have £500. You are given £200 more. You buy an object for £700 and quickly sell it on for £900. In this money transfer, after paying back the loan you have gained £200 to spend on another object.

In a chemical reaction, a similar type of energy transfer happens. Reactions that lose heat energy to the surroundings are called **exothermic reactions**. The excess energy is released in the form of heat – so the reaction warms up. You can show this on a diagram. If the energy difference is large, and it is given out very quickly, some of the energy may be given out as sound/light as part of an explosion!

Temperature rises: exothermic (energy released)

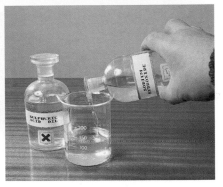

Temperature rises: exothermic (energy released)

Temperature rises: exothermic (energy released)

Temperature rises: exothermic (energy released)

Examples of exothermic reactions

Respiration in the body is another example of an exothermic reaction. It releases heat and it is this which makes us hot when we work. Some chemical reactions are exothermic.

When an exothermic reaction happens it can be measured by taking temperature readings. The temperature always rises.

Did you know?

Hand-warmers make use of an exothermic reaction involving iron salts.

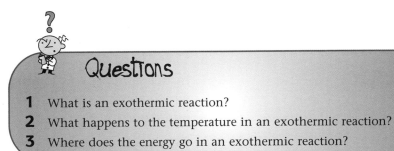

Questions

1 What is an exothermic reaction?
2 What happens to the temperature in an exothermic reaction?
3 Where does the energy go in an exothermic reaction?

Endothermic reactions

This spread should help you to

- know what 'endothermic' means
- describe what happens to the temperature in an endothermic reaction

Endothermic reaction

Sucking mints gives your mouth the feeling of being cool. This is the reverse of reactions which get hot as they proceed.

Saliva reacts with the mint sweet and energy is continually transferred from your mouth to the sweet and saliva. Your mouth cools. This energy is required to break the bonds for the reaction to continue. The reaction does not release energy but takes in more and more. This reaction is an **endothermic reaction**. Extra energy has to be transferred in from the surroundings. This makes the surroundings feel cold.

Mints are cool.

Energy: loss or gain?

Imagine you have £300 and you are given another £200 to buy an object costing £500. It is sold very quickly afterwards but for only £400. Once you have paid back the loan you have less than you started with.

In the same way as lending or borrowing money reactions which require or gain energy from the surroundings are called **endothermic reactions**.

Examples of endothermic reactions

Any reaction that feels cold is an endothermic reaction.

Using heat to decompose a substance is an endothermic reaction, for example, heat breaking down limestone into quicklime and carbon dioxide. The temperature always goes down *when* reaction products are produced.

Some other endothermic reactions: dissolving some chemical salts in water: for example potassium chloride or ammonium chloride; cooking: for example frying an egg; photosynthesis: energy is taken in from the sun to join carbon dioxide and water together to form sugar and oxygen.

Dissolving some chemicals – the beaker and solution feel colder and take in heat from the envronment

Energy taken from the environment provides the activation energy for photosynthesis to take place.

Cooking provides the activation energy for the reaction to take place.

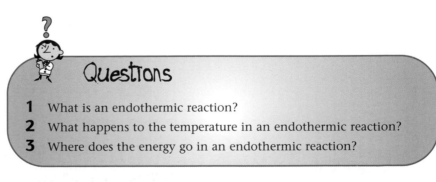

Questions

1 What is an endothermic reaction?

2 What happens to the temperature in an endothermic reaction?

3 Where does the energy go in an endothermic reaction?

Reversible reactions

Objectives

This spread should help you to

- describe what a reversible reaction is
- explain what happens in a reversible reaction
- describe how a reversible reaction can be changed

How to stand still on an escalator!

Did you know?

The symbol used to show that a reaction is reversible is ⇌

Questions

1 What is a reversible reaction?

Dynamic equilibrium

Imagine walking up an escalator which is going down. You go slower until you are walking up at the same speed as the escalator is going down. You stay in the same place.

You are moving. The escalator is moving. We call this *dynamic*. The two movements cancel each other out. You and the escalator are in *equilibrium*. This is an example of **dynamic equilibrium**. The forward motion is balanced by a backward motion.

Reversible reactions

If you add universal indicator to some acid in a beaker, it goes red. If you now add some alkali the colour changes. This is because the pH changes.

A reversible reaction: adding alkali to an acid.

If you reverse the reaction by adding acid, the reaction works in the opposite direction. This is a **reversible reaction**.

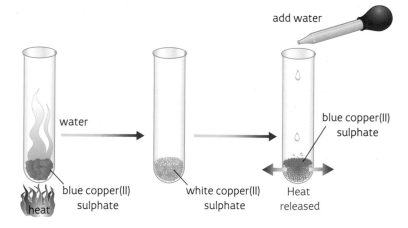

A reversible reaction.

When you heat blue copper(II) sulphate, water is driven off. The copper(II) sulphate turns white.

When you add water to the white copper(II) sulphate it turns blue again and heat is released.

Blue copper(II) sulphate is called **hydrated** (means 'with water'), white copper(II) sulphate is called **anhydrous** copper(II) sulphate ('without water').

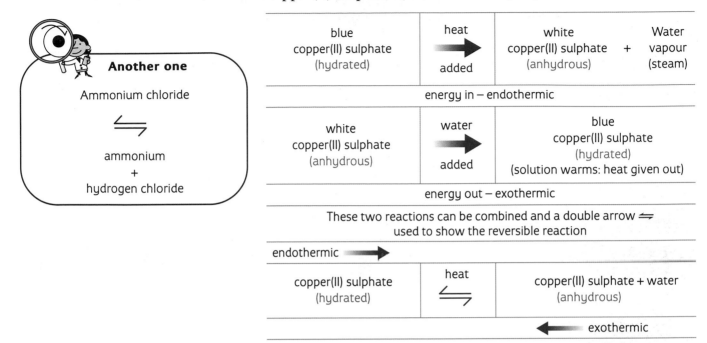

Another one

Ammonium chloride

⇌

ammonium
+
hydrogen chloride

All chemical reactions are endothermic in one direction and equally exothermic in the other direction. If you increase the temperature, the endothermic reaction will use up any extra heat. So in the above example, more white anhydrous copper(II) sulphate will be made. If you reduce the temperature the exothermic reaction will slow down.

Reactions in dynamic equilibrium

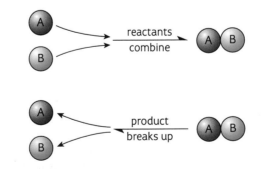

A reversible reaction is in dynamic equilibrium.

Did you know?

You could think of a reversible reaction being like the movement of birds migrating with the seasons. As the temperature falls in Britain the swallows migrate to Africa. When the temperature rises in Britain the swallows return.

Questions

2 What is equilibrium in a chemical reaction?

3 Give an example of a reversible reaction.

7.11 Water contamination

Objectives

This spread should help you to

- know why using too much fertilizer is harmful to water supplies
- describe how nitrates get into our water
- explain sources of pollution from agriculture

Animal waste products can contaminate water supplies.

Water and fertilizers

All stages of food production can cause **pollution**: growing the food, processing it, and packaging it. However, the processing and packaging produce pollutants that can be removed by water treatment processes.

More worrying is the pollution of water by nitrogen compounds that come from the rearing of animals or the growing of plants.

Animals feed on plant or animal materials. These are rich in nitrogen compounds like proteins. Some of these become protein in the animal but some are excreted as urea and ammonia. These chemicals dissolve in water in the soil and get washed into rivers.

'Muck spreading'...

Farmers spread 'muck' which is liquid animal waste on their fields. This is rich in nitrates. Other farmers spread artificial fertilizers on fields. These help plants grow because they add nitrates to the soil. Rain washes out the nitrates and urea from the muck and fertilizers into the rivers.

Questions

1 What element is found in fertilizers and proteins?

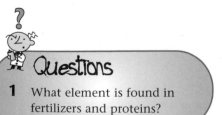

River is alive and fresh but the addition of fertilizer from the fields affects the water

Fertilizer promotes growth of algae which take over the river. Too many nitrates from fertilizers and animal waste cause eutrophication.

Eutrophication

Water which has dissolved nitrates flows into the rivers. In the rivers are many water plants and organisms called algae. The algae feed on the nitrates and grow very fast. They cover the water with a thick green blanket and stop light getting into the water. Plants need light for photosynthesis and when light is reduced the water plants die. Bacteria increase by feeding on the dead plants. They use up the dissolved oxygen, in the water. The lack of oxygen means fish will die because there is not enough oxygen for respiration. Scientists call this process **eutrophication**.

...in the end, the fish die.

Nitrates in drinking water

Scientists are also concerned about the amount of nitrates in drinking water and their effect on humans. Recent research has shown a link between nitrates in water and stomach cancer. The evidence is not clear, so much discussion goes on. Chemists continue to research and look for ways of removing nitrates from water.

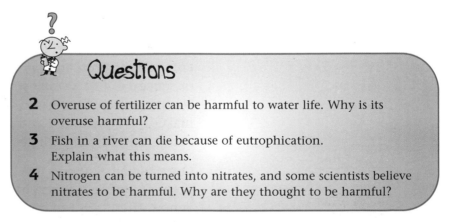

Questions

2 Overuse of fertilizer can be harmful to water life. Why is its overuse harmful?

3 Fish in a river can die because of eutrophication. Explain what this means.

4 Nitrogen can be turned into nitrates, and some scientists believe nitrates to be harmful. Why are they thought to be harmful?

Nitrogen

Objectives

This spread should help you to

- describe how nitrogen can be obtained from the air
- know how important nitrogen is
- draw the nitrogen cycle

Separating nitrogen from the air

Air is a mixture of different gases. To separate the gases from each other, air must first be turned into a liquid. Once it is a liquid, separation is easy. It is done by **fractional distillation**.

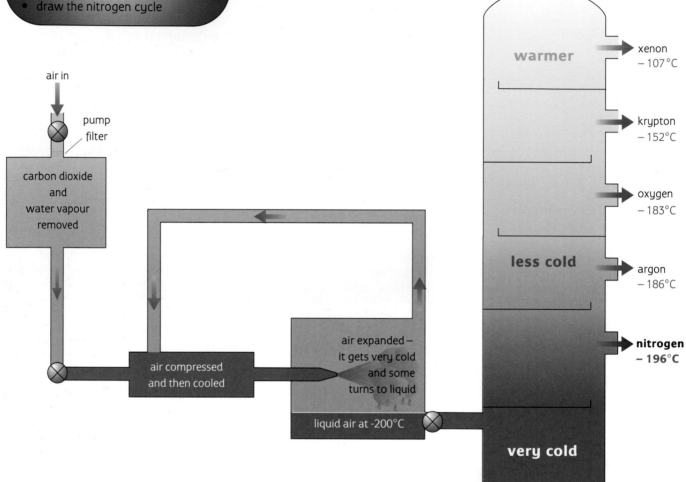

air in

pump
filter

carbon dioxide
and
water vapour
removed

air compressed
and then cooled

air expanded –
it gets very cold
and some
turns to liquid

liquid air at -200°C

warmer

xenon
− 107°C

krypton
− 152°C

oxygen
− 183°C

less cold

argon
− 186°C

**nitrogen
− 196°C**

very cold

Fractional distillation of liquid air.

First the air is filtered to remove dust and then carbon dioxide and water vapour are removed. The remaining air is compressed or squeezed into a small space while being cooled. The cold, compressed gas is released very quickly into a bigger space. This makes the gas expand and get even colder. If this is repeated many times the air will get so cold that it becomes a liquid.

Once the air is liquid it is heated up slowly. As the boiling point of each gas is reached, it boils off and is collected: first xenon, then krypton, argon, oxygen, and finally **nitrogen**. This process is called **fractional distillation**.

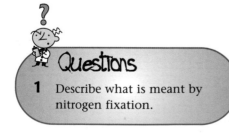

Questions

1 Describe what is meant by nitrogen fixation.

The nitrogen cycle

Nitrogen makes up 78% of the air. It is an unreactive gas and it is difficult to make it react. Yet it is an important element for building the bodies of animals and plants.

Nitrogen is an essential part of DNA, the molecule that carries the information for building living cells. Nitrogen is found in enzymes which help living things function. Most of this nitrogen comes from the action of bacteria. **Nitrifying** bacteria convert (fix) the nitrogen from air into nitrates. **Putrefying** bacteria break down dead organisms to release the nitrates, ammonia, and urea. **Denitrifying** bacteria return the nitrogen to the atmosphere

Did you know?

Humans can easily upset these cycles by producing too much carbon dioxide and nitrogen oxides, by over-using fertilizers, or by killing the bacteria in the soil.

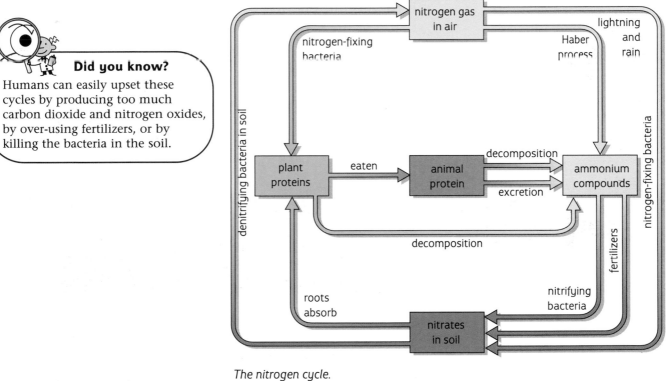

The nitrogen cycle.

Questions

2 Draw a diagram showing how liquid gases are produced.

3 Draw the nitrogen cycle and explain how it can be upset by the action of humans.

4 Why is nitrogen used on oil tankers at sea?

Nitrogen to ammonia

Objectives

This spread should help you to

- name some of the substances used as fertilizers
- describe the Haber process
- know how the chemist can change the amount of product

Plants and nitrogen

Plants grow by increasing the number of cells in their roots and stems. To grow, plants need to make proteins. To do this they need nitrogen.

Nitrogen in the air is not very reactive so plants cannot use it. The nitrogen must be got from the soil as nitrates. Some bacteria can change atmospheric nitrogen into nitrates but these are only found in some types of plants. Most plants get their nitrates from the decay of dead organisms. This does not supply enough nitrate for modern high production farming so artificial **fertilizers** are used. These are chemicals such as calcium nitrate, ammonium sulphate, ammonium nitrate, and urea.

Fertilizers must be able to dissolve in water, but not so fast that they are washed out of the soil. Ammonium nitrate dissolves very fast, but it has a high proportion of nitrogen and can pass into plants quickly. Urea dissolves more slowly and so is a slow acting fertilizer.

Fertilizers provide plants with nitrogen for growth.

Questions

1 What is the Haber process?

Making ammonia

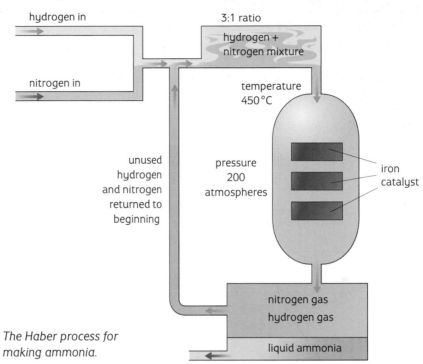

The Haber process for making ammonia.

Nitrogen gas is taken out of the air by fractional distillation. It is pumped into a mixing vessel. Hydrogen is made from steam and natural gas and is pumped in to mix with the nitrogen.

On their own these two gases will mix but will not react. They do react if the activation energy is lowered by using a catalyst.

The hydrogen reacts with nitrogen to form ammonia.

iron catalyst

nitrogen   +   hydrogen $\rightleftharpoons$ ammonia   +   heat
(gas)   +   (gas)   (gas)

$$N_2(g) \quad + \quad 3H_2(g) \quad \rightleftharpoons \quad 2NH_3(g)$$

The reaction happens at room temperature – but very, very slowly. To make it happen faster the temperature must be raised. The best temperature is 450 °C.

If the pressure is increased the reaction produces more ammonia. The best pressure to use is 200 atmospheres.

Did you know?

This process to make ammonia was developed by Fritz Haber (1868 – 1934). He sold the method to BASF, a German chemical company, in 1913 and this company helped to produce enough food to feed Germany (and to make explosives) during World War I. If they had not succeeded, the war would probably have ended before 1918.

Questions

2 How do plants obtain the nitrogen they need to grow?

3 Name some chemicals used as artificial fertilizers.

Nitric acid and fertilizers

Objectives

This spread should help you to

- describe how ammonia is changed to nitric acid
- know ammonia and nitric acid react to form a fertilizer, ammonium nitrate
- know what other elements are in fertilizers

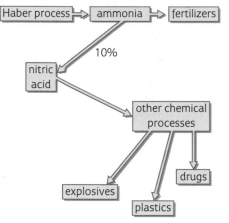

Ammonia is the starting point for making lots of useful chemicals.

Ammonia into nitric acid

Making ammonia is an important industry. It is the start for a range of other chemical industries. Ammonia production also allows a country to develop a range of explosives.

About 10% of the ammonia produced by the **Haber process** is turned into nitric acid for other processes.

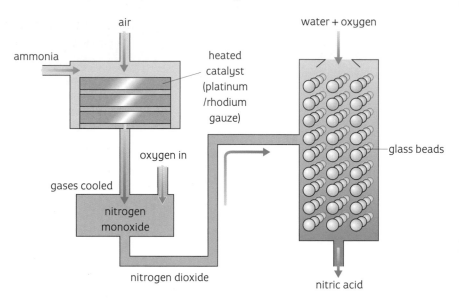

Making nitric acid.

The ammonia is mixed with air and passed over a hot catalyst. Here the ammonia is oxidized with the oxygen in the air.

ammonia + oxygen → nitrogen monoxide + water
  (gas)   (gas)   (gas)
$4NH_3(g)$ + $5O_2(g)$ → $4NO(g)$ + $6H_2O(l)$

The nitrogen monoxide gas is cooled and mixed with oxygen. Nitrogen monoxide is reactive. It reacts with the oxygen to form a very soluble gas called nitrogen dioxide.

nitrogen monoxide + oxygen → nitrogen dioxide
      (gas)   (gas)   (gas)
    $2NO(g)$ + $O_2(g)$ → $2NO_2(g)$

The nitrogen dioxide is pumped into a chamber with more oxygen where it can react and dissolve in water, forming nitric acid.

nitrogen dioxide + oxygen + water → nitric acid
    (gas)   (gas)   (liquid)   (aqueous)
  $4NO_2(g)$ + $O_2(g)$ + $2H_2O(l)$ → $4HNO_3(aq)$

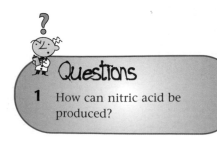

Questions

1 How can nitric acid be produced?

Ammonium nitrate fertilizer

Ammonia forms an alkali when it dissolves in water. Nitric acid is a strong acid. When an acid and an alkali react, they neutralize each other, producing a salt and water only. This is the reaction used to produce the fertilizer ammonium nitrate. The equation usually quoted is:

acid	+	alkali	→	salt	+	water
nitric acid	+	ammonia solution	→	ammonium nitrate	+	water
$HNO_3(aq)$	+	$NH_3(aq)$	→	$NH_4NO_3(aq)$		

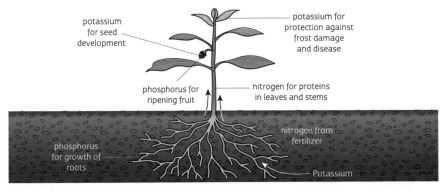

Automated fertilizer dispersal.

Other kinds of fertilizer

Plants need more than nitrogen to be healthy. To help plants grow, artificial fertilizers have other chemicals mixed in. Some of these chemicals are:

potassium for seed development

potassium for protection against frost damage and disease

phosphorus for ripening fruit

nitrogen for proteins in leaves and stems

nitrogen from fertilizer

phosphorus for growth of roots

Potassium

What plants need for healthy growth.

Did you know?

Fertilizers containing nitrogen, phosphorus, and potassium are called NPK (symbols of the elements) fertilizers. They often have numbers, such as 10N 25P 15K. These numbers are the percentages of the compounds of each element in the fertilizer.

Questions

2 What is produced when nitric acid and ammonia react?

3 What are NPK fertilizers?

This spread should help you to
- know that a symbol represents a particle
- know that more than one particle is shown by a number
- write a chemical equation for a reaction

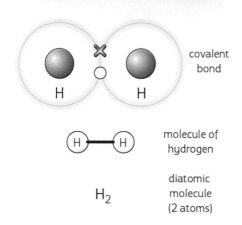

covalent bond

molecule of hydrogen

H_2

diatomic molecule (2 atoms)

A hydrogen molecule.

Chemical shorthand

To help save time and give a lot of information, chemists use a shorthand to represent a chemical reaction.

The first rule of chemical shorthand: Each element is represented by a symbol. This symbol also means one atom of the element.

Element	Symbol	Element	Symbol	Element	Symbol
Hydrogen	H	Sodium	Na	Chromium	Cr
Helium	He	Magnesium	Mg	Manganese	Mn
Lithium	Li	Aluminium	Al	Iron	Fe
Beryllium	Be	Silicon	Si	Cobalt	Co
Boron	B	Phosphorus	P	Nickel	Ni
Carbon	C	Sulphur	S	Copper	Cu
Nitrogen	N	Chlorine	Cl	Zinc	Zn
Oxygen	O	Argon	Ar	Bromine	Br
Fluorine	F	Potassium	K	Silver	Ag
Neon	Ne	Calcium	Ca	Iodine	I

Hydrogen is a gas. It is made up of molecules of two atoms sharing a pair of electrons. This is a covalent bond. Chemists show this as H_2. Sometimes the bond is shown by writing H—H.

Sodium is a metal that forms an ion by losing the outer shell electron. This makes it a positive ion and chemists show it as Na^+.

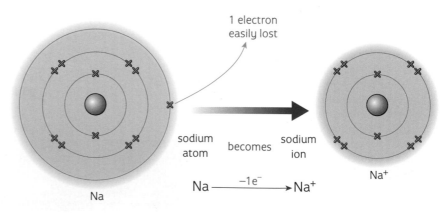

1 electron easily lost

sodium atom   becomes   sodium ion

Na^+

Na

$Na \xrightarrow{-1e^-} Na^+$

A sodium ion

This electron could be captured by a chlorine atom. This would complete its outer shell. It would make a chloride ion with a negative charge, Cl^-.

1 How many particles are represented by each of the symbols Li, P_4, Cu, O_2, Cl_2, and He?

If the sodium ion, Na$^+$, comes close to the chlorine ion, Cl$^-$, they are attracted to each other and form an ionic bond. The product is sodium chloride. The chemist writes this as follows:

$$\text{sodium ion} + \text{chloride ion} \rightarrow \text{sodium chloride}$$
$$\text{Na}^+ + \text{Cl}^- \rightarrow \text{NaCl}$$

Balancing equations

The second rule of chemical shorthand: 'You get out what you put in'. If copper is burnt in oxygen a black compound is made.

$$\text{copper (solid)} + \text{oxygen (gas)} \rightarrow \text{copper oxide (solid)}$$
$$\text{Cu} + \text{O}_2 \rightarrow \text{CuO}$$

Unbalanced

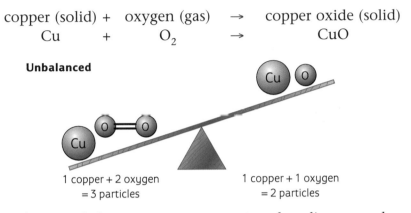

1 copper + 2 oxygen = 3 particles   1 copper + 1 oxygen = 2 particles

This does not balance, as an oxygen atom has disappeared. The chemist 'balances' the equation by writing 2Cu, meaning two copper atoms.

$$\text{copper (solid)} + \text{oxygen (gas)} \rightarrow 2 \text{ copper oxide (solid)}$$
$$\text{2Cu} + \text{O}_2 \rightarrow \text{2CuO}$$

Balanced

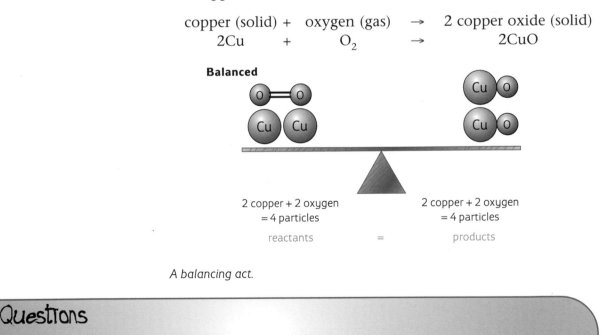

2 copper + 2 oxygen = 4 particles   2 copper + 2 oxygen = 4 particles

reactants   =   products

A balancing act.

Questions

2 What is an ionic bond?

3 What particle in the atom is involved in a chemical reaction?

Relative formula mass

Finding the mass... of a coin

Atoms are very small – too small to measure or count. When the cashier in a bank wants to count small coins, she finds the mass of the coins. Because each coin has the same mass, a set number such as 100 will always have the same mass. In chemistry the same idea is used.

Chemists add up the atomic masses of each atom in a molecule of a compound to get a number. This number *of grams of the compound* is called the **relative formula mass**.

1 coin = 1 g

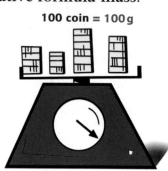
100 coin = 100 g

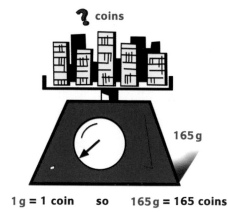
? coins

165 g

1 g = 1 coin   so   165 g = 165 coins

Counting by finding the mass.

Percentage

Mass of H	= 1 g	
Mass of Cl	= 35.5 g	
Total	= 36.5 g	
% of H	$= \frac{1}{36.5} \times 100\%$	= 2%
% of Cl	$= \frac{35.5}{36.5} \times 100\%$	= 98%

For example:

hydrogen chloride = HCl

hydrogen = 1   chlorine = 35.5   (atomic mass of elements)

1 + 35.5 = 36.5 = molecular mass of compound HCl

The relative formula mass of hydrogen chloride (HCl) has a mass of 36.5 g

Finding the relative formula mass (rfm)

Working out the relative formula mass allows chemists to be able to calculate how much of a chemical will be used in making a new substance. For example, there are many different fertilizers but which fertilizer contains the most nitrogen?

Fertilizer No 1:

ammonium sulphate $(NH_4)_2SO_4$

The relative formula mass is:

2 nitrogen atoms	$= 2 \times 14$	$=$	28
8 hydrogen atoms	$= 8 \times 1$	$=$	8
1 sulphur atom	$= 1 \times 32$	$=$	32
4 oxygen atoms	$= 4 \times 16$	$=$	64
			132

relative formula mass of $(NH_4)_2SO_4 = 132$ g

Percentage of nitrogen in ammonium sulphate is:

2 atoms of nitrogen in $(NH_4)_2SO_4$
$(= 2 \times 14 = 28)$

$\frac{28}{132} \times 100\% = 21\%$

OR

Fertilizer No 2:

ammonium nitrate $(NH_4)NO_3$

The relative formula mass is :

2 nitrogen atoms	$= 2 \times 14$	$=$	28
4 hydrogen atoms	$= 4 \times 1$	$=$	4
3 oxygen atoms	$= 3 \times 16$	$=$	48
			80

relative formula mass of $(NH_4)NO_3$ $= 80$

Percentage of nitrogen in ammonium nitrate is:

2 atoms of nitrogen in $(NH_4)NO_3$
$(= 2 \times 14 = 28)$

$\frac{28}{80} \times 100\% = 35\%$

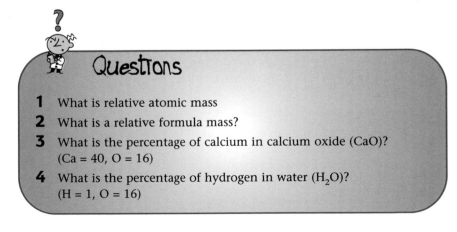

Questions

1 What is relative atomic mass
2 What is a relative formula mass?
3 What is the percentage of calcium in calcium oxide (CaO)?
   (Ca = 40, O = 16)
4 What is the percentage of hydrogen in water (H_2O)?
   (H = 1, O = 16)

Practice questions

1   Use the values of relative atomic masses to calculate the relative formula mass of:

   a   magnesium oxide (MgO)

   b   carbon monoxide (CO)

   c   nitrogen dioxide (NO_2)

   d   oxygen molecules (O_2)

   e   hydrogen chloride molecules (HCl)

   f   carbon dioxide molecules (CO_2).

2   **a**   Give two examples of slow chemical reactions and two examples of fast chemical reactions.

   b   Marble chips dissolve in dilute hydrochloric acid at a steady rate. Copy out which of the following changes would quicken up the reaction:

      i   adding more marble chips

      ii   using more concentrated acid

      iii   cooling the reacting vessel

      iv   heating the acid

      v   breaking the marble chips into smaller pieces.

3   The rectangles shown contain symbols arranged to represent molecules of:

   a   hydrogen   **b**   oxygen.

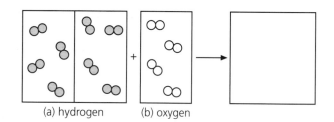

(a) hydrogen   (b) oxygen

Using the same symbols and a box similar to that given, draw in the correct number of molecules representing the new substance formed.

4   Magnesium reacts with dilute hydrochloric acid as follows:

   $Mg(s) + 2HCl(aq) \rightarrow MgCl_2(aq) + H_2(g)$

   a   A pupil carried out an experiment to investigate the rate of reaction between a piece of magnesium and 40 cm^3 of dilute hydrochloric acid at 20 °C. The acid was in excess.

      The results are shown on the graph.

   i   Copy the graph.

   ii What is the gas produced when magnesium reacts with hydrochloric acid?

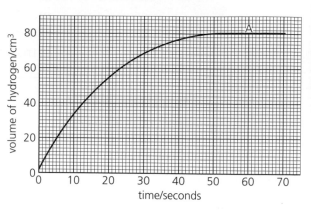

   iii What volume of gas was collected after 30 seconds?

   iv After how many seconds was the reaction just completed?

   b   The experiment was repeated using an equal mass of magnesium cut into very small pieces and a fresh 40 cm^3 of hydrochloric acid at 20 °C. The results are shown below.

time (seconds)	0	5	10	15	20	25	30	35	40	45	50
volume of gas (cm^3)	0	34	50	62	70	76	79	80	80	80	80

   i   Plot these results on to the same paper as graph A. Label the curve graph B.

   ii Which of the two lines refers to the faster reaction?

   iii Explain why the two reactions do not take place at the same rate.

   c   Which one of the following methods would increase the *final* volume of gas collected? Write the letter of the method you choose and explain your reasoning.

      A   Use of more magnesium.

      B   Use of a larger volume of dilute hydrochloric acid.

      C   Use of a more concentration solution of hydrochloric acid.

5   **a**   What happens in an exothermic reaction?

   b   Give two examples of exothermic reactions.

6 If you add potassium hydrogen carbonate powder to dilute hydrochloric acid in a beaker, the mixture fizzes up and feels cold.

   a What type of reaction is this?

   b Why is the 'energy value' positive?

   c Draw an energy graph for the reaction.

7 Write out the following passage, using correct words from the list to fill in the blanks.

List of words:

spark temperature kinetic energy oxygen activation energy potential energy

Passage: 'A gas cooker uses the burning of methane in air to supply heat. The molecules of methane possess stored _____ in the attraction between their atoms and _____ in their movement and vibrations. The same applies to the _____ molecules in the air. The average kinetic energy of the molecules is measured by the _____. In order to start the reaction, some of the molecules must be given enough energy to react. This is called the _____ and is usually supplied by a _____.'

8 a Explain how a catalyst helps a reaction.

   b Draw an energy diagram to illustrate your answer.

9 Blue copper(II) sulphate crystals turn white when heated and water (as steam) is given off. If a few drops of water are added to white anhydrous copper(II) sulphate it gets hot and turns blue.

   a Write an equation for the reactions that are happening.

   b What is the general name for such a reaction?

   c What is the definition of this general name?

10 Write out the following passage, using words from the list to fill in the blanks.

Word list

react ammonia iron methane liquid hydrogen recycled pressure catalyst nitrogen cooling

Passage: 'The Haber process combines _____ from the air with _____ made from _____ and steam, pumped at high _____ over a heated _____ made of _____. A small percentage of the reacting mixture is converted into _____ and this is removed as _____ by _____ the mixture down. The unchanged gases are _____ over the catalyst for further chances to _____.'

11 Write equations both in words and in symbols for the reactions between:

   a nitrogen and hydrogen to make ammonia

   b ammonia and air to make nitric acid

   c ammonia and nitric acid to make ammonium nitrate.

12 Give two examples of chemical pollutants which have, in the past, been allowed to escape into the sea. What was the effect in each case?

13 Calculate the relative molecular mass and the percentage of carbon present in:

   a carbon dioxide CO_2

   b glucose $C_6H_{12}O_6$

   c limestone $CaCO_3$

   (Note C = 12 , O = 16, H = 1, Ca = 40)

14 Draw two large diagrams to show:

   a how the gases in the air are separated

   b how nitrogen moves through the environment as different compounds

15 a Briefly describe the industrial extraction of nitrogen from the air.

   b Give one industrial and one non-industrial use of nitrogen.

   c What is the approximate percentage of nitrogen found in the atmosphere?

   d How is ammonia formed from nitrogen gas?

   e How is ammonia changed into nitric acid?

Key words

activation energy	amount of energy needed to be given to start a reaction
anhydrous	a substance which has had the water removed
bacteria – denitrifying, nitrifying, putrefying	single celled organisms which release or fix nitrogen
biotechnology	the use of biological chemical like enzymes to make new chemicals
boiling point	the temperature a liquid turns into a gas
catalysts	a substance that speeds up a reaction but remains unchanged throughout the reaction
chlorophyll	a green pigment chemical found in plants that catalysis photosynthesis
decomposition	when a compound breaks up into simple compounds
endothermic reaction	a reaction in which heat energy is taken in from the surroundings
enzyme	a natural catalyst produced by a living organism
equilibrium	when a chemical goes forwards and backwards and the two balance each other
eutrophication	when oxygen is removed by a living organism like bacteria starving another organism like fish in a river
exothermic reactions	a reaction in which heat energy is transferred to the surroundings
expands	when a solid or liquid is heated and the volume increases

explosion	rapid combustion
fermentation	when a sugar is broken down by an enzyme to form alcohol and carbon dioxide
fertilizers	means of returning nitrogen and other minerals to the soil by chemicals, some artificial, some natural
Haber process	he process of producing ammonia from nitrogen and hydrogen by use of catalysts, pressure and heat
hydrated	when crystals have water locked into the structure to help hold the chemicals together
kinetic energy	energy due to movement
melting point	the temperature a solid melts into a liquid
relative formula mass	the mass of each atom in a substance formula added together, in g
neutralization	When a base and an acid react to form a salt and water
oxidation	(i) when an element combines with oxygen to form an oxide
	(ii) when a negative ion loses electrons to form an atom
pH	the strength of an acid pH scale runs from 0 – 14
photosynthesis	when chlorophyll catalyses the combination of carbon dioxide and water to form starch and oxygen
relative atomic mass (RAM)	the mass of an element compared with the isotope of carbon 12
reversible reaction	a reaction that can be reversed

synthesis   when chemicals join together to form a new substance

temperature   measure of the kinetic energy in a substances molecules

thermal decom- position   when a chemical breaks down into simpler compounds with heat

Module **8**

Materials have the properties they have because of the type and arrangement of their atoms. Diamonds are hard because of the way their atoms are bonded together. Fireworks are coloured because of the elements they contain. Using different elements will produce different colours.

Origins of the elements

1

The universe began with the 'big bang'. Immediately, the Universe was full of radiation and particles, soon including the elements hydrogen and helium. The first stars were made almost entirely of these two elements.

The Big Bang

6

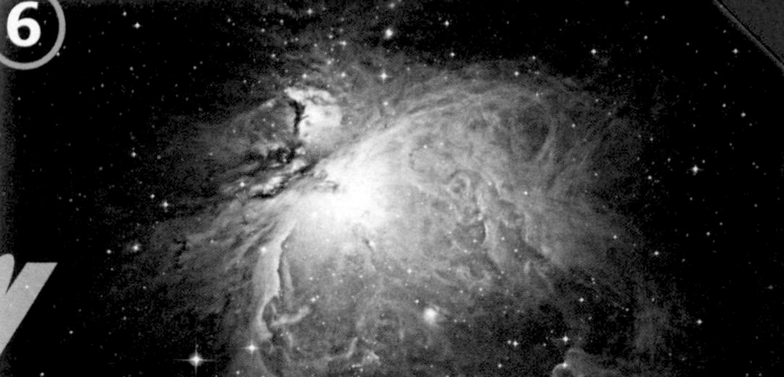

Such beautiful nebulas as this, the Orion nebula (you can just see it faintly with the naked eye in the constellation Orion), are enriched by the elements created in supernovas. Deep inside, new stars are born and begin to shine.

7

Explosion

Stars continue to grow old and die, the higher-mass ones creating more elements in the process. New stars are born out of these elements.

Talking point

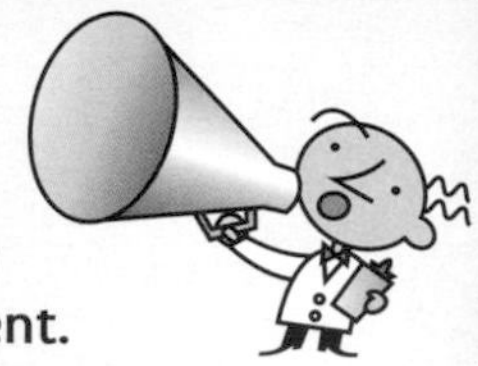

There is more hydrogen in the universe than any other element. From what you know about the structure of atoms, can you think why this is?

② Stars form in regions such as this, part of the Eagle nebula (a cloud of gas and particles). They generate energy first by converting hydrogen into helium. When the hydrogen begins to run out, the helium is converted into carbon and oxygen. Low-mass stars get no further than this in producing elements.

③ This star, called Sher 25, has about 25 times the mass of our Sun and is hundreds of times bigger. Such high-mass stars go on to produce even heavier elements, up to iron.

⑤ This is the Crab nebula. It is all that remains of a supernova seen by Chinese astronomers in 1054. (The actual explosion took place 6000 years earlier, because the light took that long to reach Earth.)

④

Explosion

These high-mass stars have violent, explosive endings called supernovas. One supernova can be brighter than all the other 100 billion stars in a galaxy! Supernovas throw the heavier elements out into space and also create and throw out even heavier elements than iron.

⑧ Some of these elements form materials that clump together in smaller lumps, forming solid or gas planets, like these members of our own Solar System. There may be many more planets around other stars.

9 All the elements necessary for life were made inside massive stars and spread throughout the Universe by supernova explosions.

We come from the stars!

Particles and materials

Objectives

This spread should help you to

- know that matter is made up of particles
- know that particles are always on the move
- describe solids, liquids, and gases.

Particles in solid materials

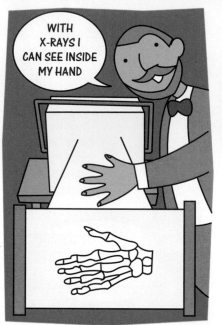

Just over a hundred years ago Wilhelm Röntgen (1845–1923) discovered X-rays.

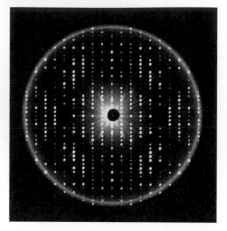

An X-ray of a crystal showing the pattern of the atoms in the crystal.

William Bragg (1862–1942) and his son Lawrence Bragg (1890–1971) produced X-ray photographs of crystals. The pattern seen by the Braggs shows us that solids have particles arranged in a regular order. They are held together by forces of attraction. This attraction means the particles can only vibrate about a fixed position.

This vibrations get bigger when the solid is heated. The particles do not get any bigger. But they do need more space for their vibration. The solid will get bigger. The increase in spaces means the substance **expands**.

Particles vibrate — attractive forces stop particles moving out of position

Particles vibrate more — attractive forces stop particles moving out of position

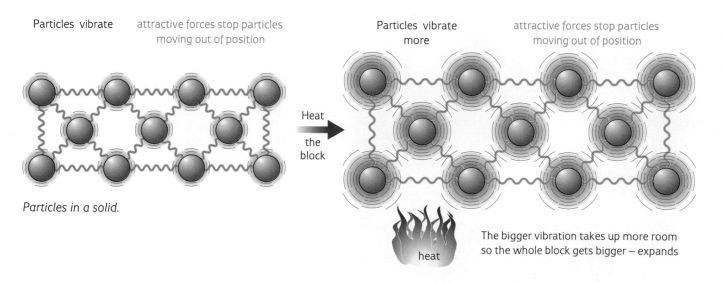

Particles in a solid.

Heat the block

The bigger vibration takes up more room so the whole block gets bigger – expands

heat

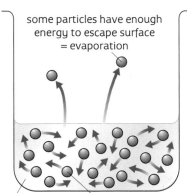

some particles have enough energy to escape surface = evaporation

The volume does not increase very much

Particles vibrate so much the attractive forces are not strong enough.

Particles in a liquid vibrate and can roll over each other.

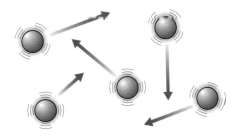

Particles in a gas vibrate and move freely.

Liquids and rolling particles

As a solid is heated the forces of attraction get weaker. This means the pattern is lost. The distance between the particles does not increase very much. The particles roll over each other.

The solid has **melted** to form a liquid. This means the particles have more moving (kinetic) energy.

Some particles have so much moving energy they can escape from the surface. This is known as **evaporation**. Because only a few particles have enough energy to escape, liquids evaporate very slowly.

If the energy of the particles in the liquid is increased by heat or light or other means, the particles move faster. The distance between the particles gets bigger and the attraction is very small. The particles can move and spread out to fill the space. When lots of particles move very fast and escape the liquid it is called **boiling** and the liquid forms a gas.

Pure substances

If all the particles in a substance are the same, the substance is **pure**. A pure substance will melt at a definite temperature. This is called the **melting point**. It will also boil at a certain temperature (the **boiling point**). Different substances have different melting and boiling points. For example, pure water (as ice) melts at 0°C and boils to steam at 100°C.

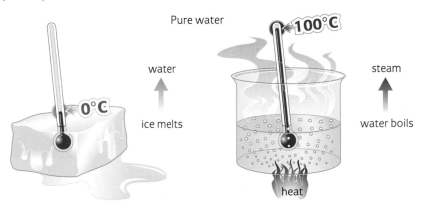

Pure water

water

ice melts

0°C

100°C

steam

water boils

heat

Ice melts at 0°C; water boils at 100°C.

Questions

1 Draw three diagrams: one of a solid, one of a liquid, and one of a gas.

2 What is different about the way the particles are arranged in each of them?

3 What happens to the particles when the material is heated?

4 What is a pure substance?

Evidence for the atom

Objectives

You should be able to:

- explain why the idea of the atom became important in science
- give some of the important evidence for the idea of atoms
- describe the structure of an atom

Strange beliefs

By about 420 BCE the Greek thinkers had come up with various ideas about the stuff or matter around us. Thales suggested that all things are made of water. Empedocles decided that there are four elements that make up matter. They are earth, water, air, and fire.

Leucippus (480–420 BCE) and his pupil Democritus thought that everything was made of tiny bits named particles. Democritus (460–370 BCE) said that fire hurts you because it is made up of tiny sharp pyramids or tetrahedrons. It is the points of those bits that hurt. Water is made up of icosahedrons (20 sided) that can roll over each other. Earth is made up of cubes that fit closely together and so are hard to move.

Democritus thought (wrongly) that everything was made from different shaped particles.

Democritus built a **thought model** to help explain his ideas. Modern scientists also do this, and in chemistry you will meet many thought models. These help scientists to solve problems.

Always the same quantities

John Dalton (1766–1844) was always experimenting with chemicals. One of the most important things he did was to weigh the materials before and after his experiments. From this he realized that substances always react together in definite proportions. This fits in with the idea of **atoms**.

Did you know?

Leucippus came up with the idea that these particles were uncuttable or indivisible. The Greek word for uncuttable is 'atomos'. So the particles were named **atoms**.

Rutherford's ideas changed the way we think about atoms.

Dalton's ideas were:

- matter is made up of small particles called atoms;
- atoms cannot be destroyed or created;
- atoms of a particular element are all exactly alike and different from atoms of another element;
- when elements combine, whole numbers of atoms combine.

Shooting at empty space

Dalton's idea of the atom made scientists think of them as billiard balls. When Joseph John (J. J.) Thomson (1856–1940) discovered **electrons** he thought they were stuck in the atom like currants in a bun. The electron is very small and has a negative charge.

In 1909 Ernest Rutherford (1871–1937) and his students fired small particles at a piece of gold foil. This is like hitting tennis balls at a wall. If the atoms are solid, the particles will bounce off. But to Rutherford's surprise, most of the particles went through. This meant atoms are not solid balls. The wall was more like a wire link fence with big holes.

Even more surprising, Rutherford discovered that positively charged bits were knocked out of the atoms. These positive charged particles he called **protons**. An atom has no charge. The negative charge on an electron (–1) is the same size as the positive charge on a proton (+1). So the number of electrons must equal the number of protons. Their charges cancel out.

Electrons weigh hardly anything. So the mass of an atom should be almost equal to the mass of all its protons. But James Chadwick (1891–1974) found that the mass of an atom was always *more* than the total mass of its protons. There must be something else in the atom! Chadwick carried out more experiments, and in 1932 he discovered the **neutron**.

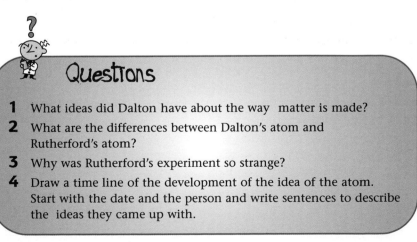

Questions

1. What ideas did Dalton have about the way matter is made?
2. What are the differences between Dalton's atom and Rutherford's atom?
3. Why was Rutherford's experiment so strange?
4. Draw a time line of the development of the idea of the atom. Start with the date and the person and write sentences to describe the ideas they came up with.

8.04

Discovery of the elements

Ancient times – fire helps discover some elements

Volcanoes are Nature's chemistry set. Minerals and metals are found in the boiling and bubbling lava and heated rocks. Long ago, people associated sulphur with fire – fire and brimstone (sulphur). Prehistoric people found sulphur deposited near volcanoes.

Gold, silver, and copper were also discovered in prehistoric times. They can be found as 'native' metals. Another element that was known thousands of years ago is carbon. It was produced as charcoal by slow burning of wood.

People used to keep fires burning for days at very high temperatures to dry and fire clay for making pots. During this time some strange things happened to the rocks surrounding the fire. Molten (melted) metal flowed from the rocks.

Many rocks contain ores of metals. If the rocks fell into the fire, the heat and the carbon reduced the ores to metals. From this came metals such as lead, tin, copper, and iron. This is one way in which metals might have been discovered: historians do not really know.

Mercury was also known by the ancient Greeks and was a curiosity because it was a liquid. The Chinese often purified mercury by distillation.

The alchemist's era

Hennig Brandt was an alchemist, one of the earliest chemists. Brandt was looking for a 'philosopher's stone', a mythical substance that would turn base metals into gold. In 1669 he isolated a pale waxy substance from urine, which turned out to be not the 'philosopher's stone' but the element phosphorus. Between 1200 and 1750 alchemists discovered the following elements: arsenic, antimony, bismuth, zinc, platinum, phosphorus, and cobalt.

An alchemist excited at phosphorus glowing in the dark, in a painting in 1771.

Davy – discoverer of elements

Humphrey Davy (1778–1829) was one of the best scientists of the early 1800s. He worked at the Royal Institution, where people flocked to hear him talk. His talks were so popular that the world's first one-way street system was set up in Albemarle Street, London to deal with the traffic.

Talking point

What elements can you think of that you come into contact with every day?

1807 Royal Institution

molten potassium

+ −

molten potassium salt

1807 Royal Institution

In 1807 I also discovered sodium by using electrolysis.

1808 Royal Institution

In 1808 I used electrolysis to discover calcium, magnesium, barium, and strontium.

Other discoverers of elements

I discovered cerium in 1803, selenium in 1818, silicon in 1824, and thorium in 1829. I also found that we could group elements in families. I used the name 'halogen'.

Jöns Jacob Berzelius (1779–1848)

You will know me as the inventor of the Bunsen burner. However, my work with Gustav Kirchhoff helped us to discover rubidium and caesium.

Robert Bunsen (1811–1899)

Working as husband and wife, we discovered the radioactive element polonium in 1898. In 1910 Marie discovered radium.

Hi. During World War 2 we were working on the atomic bomb and during that work we discovered plutonium in 1944, since when we have discovered nine more radioactive elements.

Glenn Seaborg (1912–1999)

Marie and Pierre Curie (1867–1934) & (1859–1906)

Looking at different atoms

This spread should help you to
- draw an atom
- work out the number of particles in an atom
- know that the number of protons equals the number of electrons in an atom

Did you know?

Electrons move so fast we cannot tell exactly where they are.

Protons are **p**ositive (p⁺), **n**eutrons are **n**eutral (n⁰), and **e**lectrons are negative (e⁻).

The atom

Ernest Rutherford (1871–1937) developed a model of the atom in which a central **nucleus** made of protons and neutrons tightly held together by a strong force is surrounded by electrons in **orbits**. Niels Bohr (1885–1962) improved on this model. He came up with the significant idea that electrons in atoms are found only in layers like an onion skin around the nucleus.

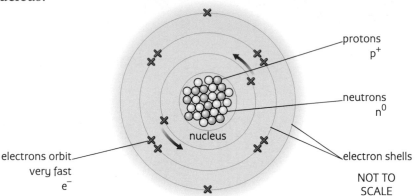

protons
p⁺

neutrons
n⁰

nucleus

electrons orbit very fast
e⁻

electron shells

NOT TO SCALE

A model of an atom.

For an atom:
the number of protons = the number of electrons
the number of protons = the **atomic number**

proton

neutron

electron

Scientists compare atomic particles by giving protons and neutrons a mass of 1. Electrons have almost no mass.

Did you know?

To be able to move quickly around the nucleus, electrons have to be very light. In fact, 1836 electrons have the same mass as one proton.

Mass of atoms

Electrons are very small, they move very fast, they are very light. Most of the mass of the atom is in the **nucleus**. It is not easy to measure the mass of tiny particles.

$$\textbf{atomic mass number} = \binom{\text{number of}}{\text{protons}} + \binom{\text{number of}}{\text{neutrons}}$$

To measure the mass of atoms scientists compare atoms of different elements. They do this by using a mass spectrometer.

Because they are small, the masses of atoms are not generally measured directly but are compared to a standard. That standard is carbon. The **relative atomic mass** (RAM) of an element is the mass of one atom of that element relative to $\frac{1}{12}$ the mass of one atom of carbon.

Some relative atomic masses

hydrogen	1.0	carbon	12.0	sodium	23.0	sulphur	32.1
helium	4.0	nitrogen	14.0	magnesium	24.3	chlorine	35.5
lithium	6.9	oxygen	16.0	aluminium	27.0	argon	39.9
beryllium	9.0	fluorine	19.0	silicon	28.1	potassium	39.1
boron	10.8	neon	20.2	phosphorus	31.0	calcium	40.1

Isotopes

But the mass of an atom is the number of protons and neutrons in its nucleus (a whole number). How come the relative atomic mass of some elements is *not* a whole number?

All the atoms of an element have the same number of protons and electrons (atomic number). But some atoms of an element may have a different number of neutrons.

Two or more atoms that have the same atomic number but different numbers of neutrons are called **isotopes**.

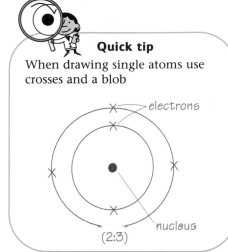

Quick tip

When drawing single atoms use crosses and a blob

electrons
nucleus
(2:3)

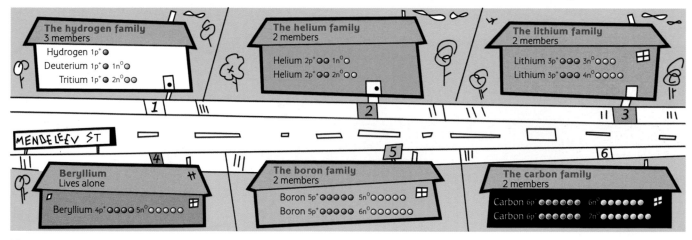

Mendeleev Street: a way of thinking about elements.

Think of a row of houses in a street. A single family lives in each house but the number in each family is different. Elements can have different numbers of isotopes. A sample of an element will contain atoms with different atomic mass numbers. The relative atomic mass is the average of the atomic mass numbers of all those atoms.

Questions

1 Draw a diagram of an atom and label the electron, nucleus, proton, and neutron.

2 What is the atomic number?

3 What is the atomic mass number?

Atom viewers, accelerators, and smashers

An optical microscope

An animal cell

The human egg cell is the size of a full stop. A nerve cell in a giraffe's neck is over 2 m long.

small

Protons are about 2000 times heavier than electrons.

A proton

smaller still than even smaller still

A neutron

Back to everyday life

It is not only scientists who use particle accelerators. You use them when you play your favourite computer game on your television set. You are manipulating beams of electrons to strike the screen.

Doctors use particle accelerators to treat cancer. Electrons fired at a metal produce X-rays which can be used to treat tumours.

Industry uses them to make microchips for computer processors or memory. They also use electron beams for welding and drilling metals.

Archaeologists use them to analyse materials and to date them.

Talking point

What are the differences in size between an animal cell, a molecule of DNA, an atom, and a nucleus?

DNA

A scanning electron microscope (it uses electrons instead of light)

smaller still

There are as many molecules in a teaspoon of water as there are teaspoons of water in the Atlantic Ocean.

An atom

Atoms are 99.99% empty space.

An electron

even smaller still

An atomic nucleus

The nucleus is 100 000 times smaller than the whole atom.

A particle accelerator can be used to break up atoms

Objectives

This spread should help you to

- describe where to find the electrons in an atom
- describe how electrons form shells (energy levels) in an atom
- know how many electrons are in the first three shells

The electron

An atom consists of a nucleus and a number of electrons in orbits around the nucleus. These orbits are called **shells**.

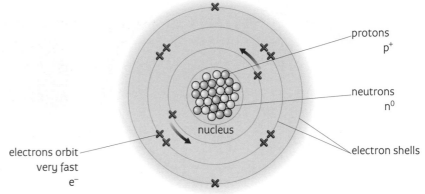

protons
p+

neutrons
n⁰

electron shells

electrons orbit very fast
e⁻

nucleus

Model of an atom.

The nucleus has a positive charge because of the protons in it. It is also very heavy because the protons and neutrons are heavy. Electrons are very light. They orbit very fast around the nucleus. Electrons are negatively charged. They are attracted to the nucleus by the positive charge of the proton.

Electron shells (or *energy levels*)

Electrons form clouds or shells at a particular energy level. In each shell there is a limit to the number of electrons. In the inner shell there is room for only two electrons.

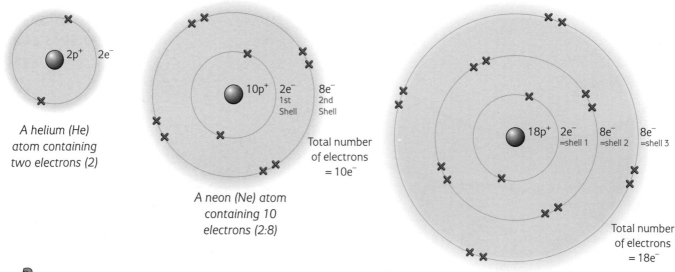

$2p^+$ $2e^-$

A helium (He) atom containing two electrons (2)

$10p^+$ $2e^-$ 1st Shell $8e^-$ 2nd Shell

Total number of electrons $= 10e^-$

A neon (Ne) atom containing 10 electrons (2:8)

$18p^+$ $2e^-$ =shell 1 $8e^-$ =shell 2 $8e^-$ =shell 3

Total number of electrons $= 18e^-$

An argon (Ar) atom containing 18 electrons (2:8:8)

Questions

1 What charge does an electron have?

If the atom has more than two electrons, the extra electrons must go in the next shell. This shell can hold up to eight electrons. Electrons in this second shell are shown in pairs. When this second shell has eight electrons, it is full. The next electron must go into the third shell. When the second or third shell has eight electrons, the atom is very stable and slow to react. All atoms would like to complete their outer shell by having two electrons (if it is the first shell) or eight in other shells. The higher the shell, the higher the energy level.

Drawing atoms with electron shells

It often helps to draw pictures of atoms to understand how they are made up. Here are some simple rules:

1 Put the protons in the nucleus at the centre as p^+.
2 Put the neutrons in the nucleus at the centre as n^0.
3 Draw the electrons in shells around the nucleus.
4 Shell rules. Shell 1 can only hold two electrons. Shell 2 can only hold eight electrons. Shell 3 holds eight electrons.

Note: the table shows information for one isotope of the element.

Element	Symbol	Number of protons	Number of neutrons	Shell 1	Shell 2	Shell 3	Shell 4	Written as...	Total number of electrons
hydrogen	H	1	0	1				1	= 1
helium	He	2	2	2				2	= 2
lithium	Li	3	4	2	1			2:1	= 3
beryllium	Be	4	5	2	2			2:2	= 4
boron	B	5	6	2	3			2:3	= 5
carbon	C	6	6	2	4			2:4	= 6
nitrogen	N	7	7	2	5			2:5	= 7
oxygen	O	8	8	2	6			2:6	= 8
fluorine	F	9	10	2	7			2:7	= 9
neon	Ne	10	10	2	8			2:8	= 10
sodium	Na	11	12	2	8	1		2:8:1	= 11
magnesium	Mg	12	12	2	8	2		2:8:2	= 12
aluminium	Al	13	14	2	8	3		2:8:3	= 13
silicon	Si	14	14	2	8	4		2:8:4	= 14
phosphorus	P	15	16	2	8	5		2:8:5	= 15
sulphur	S	16	16	2	8	6		2:8:6	= 16
chlorine	Cl	17	18	2	8	7		2:8:7	= 17
argon	Ar	18	22	2	8	8		2:8:8	= 18
potassium	K	19	20	2	8	8	1	2:8:8:1	= 19
calcium	Ca	20	20	2	8	8	2	2:8:8:2	= 20

Questions

2 What charge does the nucleus have?
3 How many electrons are found in the first shell and in the second shell when they are full?

Ions and ionic bonds

Objectives

This spread should help you to

- describe an ionic bond
- draw a diagram of an ionic bond
- know that one ion is positive and the other ion is negative

Atoms of elements join to form compounds. The atoms are held together by **bonds**. It is sometimes possible to see these bonds using a special microscope called an atomic force microscope.

An image taken using an atomic force microscope of gold atoms on a graphite surface. The carbon atoms are bonded into flat crystals.

Push and pull

Bonding between atoms is the result of opposite charges **attracting** and like charges **repelling**. If two atoms come near, their nuclei repel each other. Their electrons repel each other. The nucleus of one atom attracts the electrons of the other atom.

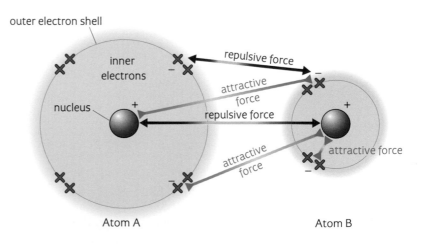

Attractive and repulsive forces.

If two atoms collide with each other, they normally bounce apart. Whether they bond depends on the energy the atoms have when they collide.

In **ionic bonding** one atom loses an outer electron altogether to a different atom. This happens if the pull from one nucleus is so strong that it pulls an electron off the other atom.

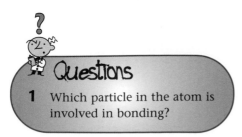

Questions

1 Which particle in the atom is involved in bonding?

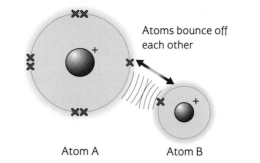

Atoms bounce off each other

Atom A   Atom B

A gentle collision: there is not enough energy for the electrons to make a bond.

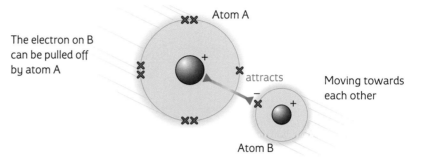

Atom A

The electron on B can be pulled off by atom A

attracts

Moving towards each other

Atom B

Here the atoms are moving with more energy. They get close enough for the electron on atom B to be pulled off atom A.

Ionic bond = electron gain and electron loss

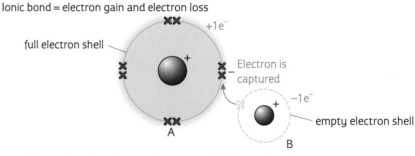

+1e⁻

full electron shell

Electron is captured

A

−1e⁻

empty electron shell

B

*Atom A has taken the electron from atom B. This makes A a **negative ion** and B a **positive ion**.*

Summary

An ion is a charged particle. You can think of an ionic bond as made up of two parts: a positive ion; and a negative ion 'joined' together.

The outer electron in atom B is held only weakly. Atom A can take an electron away. This makes it a positively charged **ion**. Atom A has gained an extra electron, making it negatively charged. It is a negative ion.

By gaining an electron, atom A now has 8 electrons in its outer shell. This makes it more stable. Atom B had only 1 electron in its outer shell. Losing that electron makes it more stable. (They appear to have the shell structure of noble gases.)

Questions

2 What happens to the 'bonding' particle when an ionic bond is formed?

Ionic crystals (1)

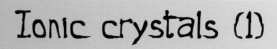

Objectives
This spread should help you to
- know why ionic substances conduct when melted or in solution
- describe how an ionic crystal is formed from oppositely charged ions

Revisiting the ionic bond

When an atom loses an electron to another atom it changes. The loss of one electron leaves the atom with all its protons but minus an electron. This makes an atom with a positive charge called an ion. An atom that gains an electron becomes a negative ion with a strong negative charge.

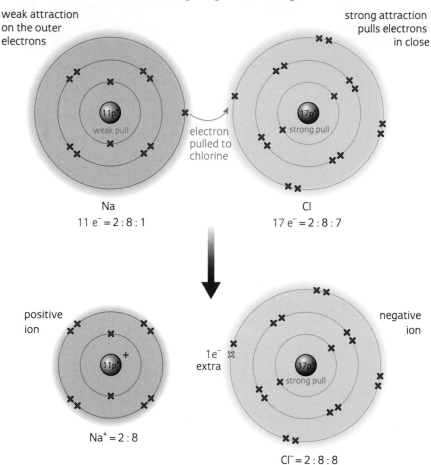

weak attraction on the outer electrons

strong attraction pulls electrons in close

11p
weak pull

17p
strong pull

electron pulled to chlorine

Na
11 e⁻ = 2 : 8 : 1

Cl
17 e⁻ = 2 : 8 : 7

positive ion

negative ion

11p +

1e⁻ extra

17p
strong pull

Na⁺ = 2 : 8

Cl⁻ = 2 : 8 : 8

Sodium chloride ionic bond = attraction between a positive sodium ion and a negative chloride ion. (Now they have the electronic structure of a noble gas.)

Sodium is a metal and chlorine is a non-metal, and when they react, electrons are lost by sodium and gained by chlorine. The reaction is explosive. Sodium is a reactive grey metal; chlorine is a smelly poisonous gas. The ionic compound they form is white crystals of sodium chloride.

Another pair of elements that form ionic bonds are magnesium and oxygen. Magnesium is a grey metal while oxygen is a colourless gas. Magnesium burns in oxygen to form a white solid called magnesium oxide.

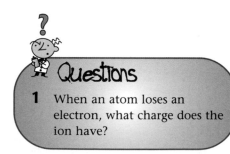

Questions

1 When an atom loses an electron, what charge does the ion have?

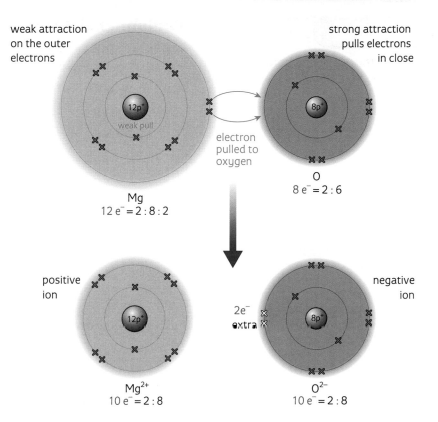

weak attraction on the outer electrons

Mg
12 e⁻ = 2 : 8 : 2

weak pull

electron pulled to oxygen

strong attraction pulls electrons in close

O
8 e⁻ = 2 : 6

positive ion

Mg²⁺
10 e⁻ = 2 : 8

2e⁻ extra

negative ion

O²⁻
10 e⁻ = 2 : 8

Magnesium oxide ionic bond = attraction between positive magnesium ion and a negative oxide ion.

Crystals

When a single positive ion comes close to a single negative ion, they attract. This strong attraction is the **ionic bond**. It is so strong that it pulls the ions close together. The ions arrange themselves so that a positive or negative ion is surrounded by oppositely charged ions. This is repeated until a giant structure is created.

A giant structure like this is called an ionic **crystal**. The ions are held in place by the surrounding ions. They have high melting and boiling points.

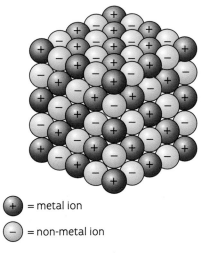

+ = metal ion

− = non-metal ion

A ionic crystal.

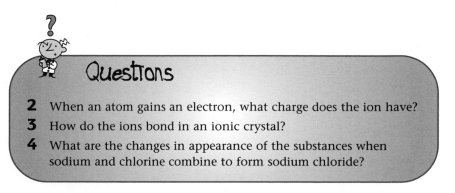

Questions

2 When an atom gains an electron, what charge does the ion have?

3 How do the ions bond in an ionic crystal?

4 What are the changes in appearance of the substances when sodium and chlorine combine to form sodium chloride?

Ionic crystals (2)

Did you know?

Sodium chloride ('salt') is important for many reactions in our bodies. The sodium ion is important for cells, blood, and muscles.
How much we take in is important. Too much can give us high blood pressure. Some of the highest salt eaters are the Japanese, who eat on average 20 grams a day. The lowest eaters of salt are the Yanomamo tribe in Venezuela, who eat almost no salt.

Sodium chloride

If A is a chlorine atom, it gains an electron and becomes a negatively charged chlor*ide* ion, Cl^-. If B is a sodium atom, it loses an electron and becomes a positively charged sodium ion, Na^+.

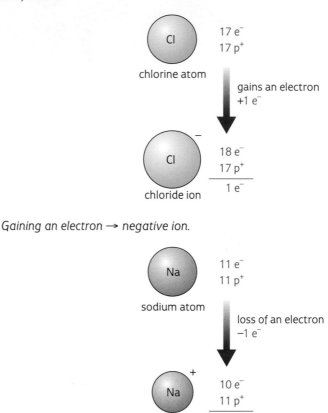

Gaining an electron → negative ion.

Losing an electron → positive ion.

Because the ions have opposite charges, they are attracted to each other. This is an **ionic bond**. They make the compound sodium chloride – common salt.

Ionic bonds are usually between metals and non-metals. In non-metals the electrons are held in close. In metals the outer electrons are held only loosely and are easily lost.

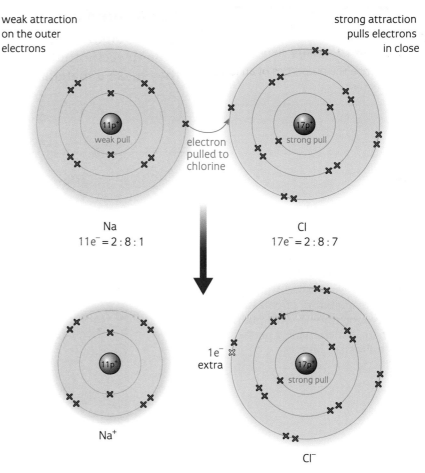

weak attraction on the outer electrons

strong attraction pulls electrons in close

11p⁺
weak pull

electron pulled to chlorine

17p⁺
strong pull

Na
$11e^- = 2 : 8 : 1$

Cl
$17e^- = 2 : 8 : 7$

11p⁺

1e⁻ extra

17p⁺
strong pull

Na⁺

Cl⁻

Ionic bond = attraction between a positive ion and a negative ion.

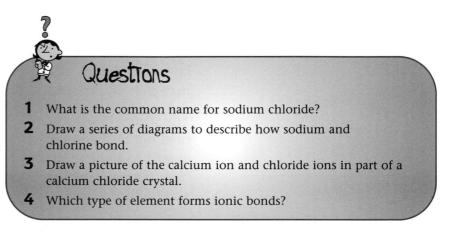

Questions

1 What is the common name for sodium chloride?

2 Draw a series of diagrams to describe how sodium and chlorine bond.

3 Draw a picture of the calcium ion and chloride ions in part of a calcium chloride crystal.

4 Which type of element forms ionic bonds?

Ionic crystals (3)

Compounds

Ionic compounds have strong bonds with the ions pulled close to each other. Because the ions are close and held tightly, they make a material that is hard.

Did you know?

Our grandparents used to use crystals to make their clothes look whiter. Strangely these crystals were blue! They were called laundry blue and were a mixture of potassium hexacyanoferrate(II) with iron(III) sulphate, which made a pigment called Prussian Blue.

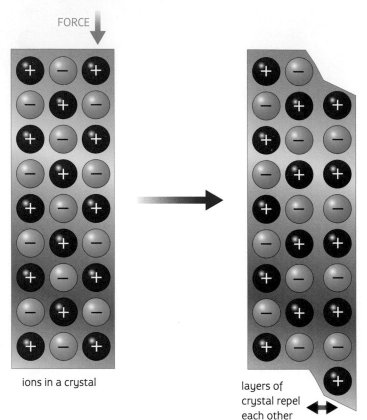

FORCE

ions in a crystal

layers of crystal repel each other

If you hit an **ionic crystal**, the layers of ions slide over each other. Positive ions find themselves next to positive ions. The layers repel each other, making the material break up. So ionic materials are brittle and difficult to bend.

The strong bonds in ionic substances mean that the ions are held tightly by electrostatic attraction. To make these ions fall apart you have to make them vibrate very fast. This requires high temperatures, so ionic compounds have high melting and boiling points.

Melted ionic compounds conduct electricity because the ions are electrically charged and able to move. When ionic substances dissolve in water, the ions can move freely. So solutions of ionic substances conduct electricity.

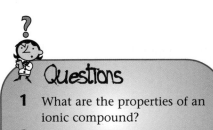

Questions

1 What are the properties of an ionic compound?

2 Why are ionic crystals brittle and difficult to bend?

Symbols

Compounds are shown by combining the symbols of the elements in the compound. For example, sodium is shown as Na. A sodium ion is shown as Na$^+$. Chlorine atoms are shown as Cl. A chloride ion is shown as Cl$^-$. The ionic compound sodium chloride is shown as NaCl.

Compound ions

Some ions are formed from molecules of compounds that lose or gain electrons. They are called compound ions.

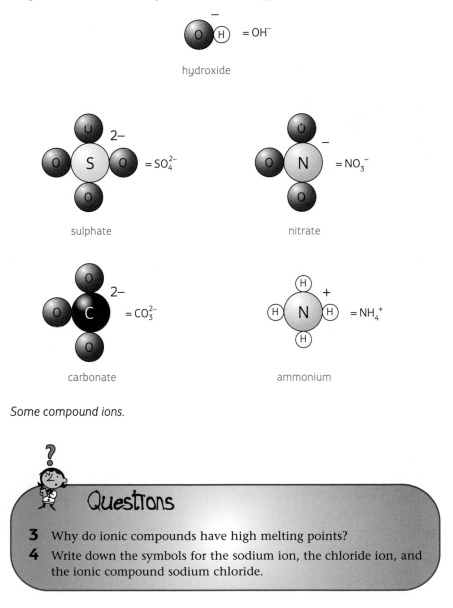

hydroxide

sulphate

nitrate

carbonate

ammonium

Some compound ions.

Questions

3 Why do ionic compounds have high melting points?

4 Write down the symbols for the sodium ion, the chloride ion, and the ionic compound sodium chloride.

Properties of metals

Objectives

This spread should help you to

- know that metals have bonds involving electrons
- draw a diagram of the metal bond
- describe some of the properties of metals

More than three-quarters (about 80) of the elements are metals. They are mainly found in Groups 1 and 2 and in the transition block. They are generally strong, hard, and easy to shape into objects, and they have high melting and boiling points. They conduct electricity and heat better than other solids. Why?

The metallic bond

The answer lies in the way the metal atoms bond together. Metal atoms have just one or two electrons in their outer shells. They cannot fill their outer shells by swapping electrons, as in an ionic bond, or sharing electrons, as in a covalent bond. Instead the atoms are packed tightly together and all the outer electrons are shared between them. A metal is a giant array of atoms surrounded by a 'sea' of electrons.

Copper atom
metal

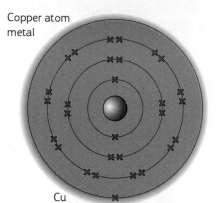

Cu
1 electron in outer shell – can be removed easily

Copper atoms in a giant metal structure

The outer electrons can flow freely around the copper atoms. ('Transition' metals like copper can have 18 electrons in the third shell.)

Properties of metals

- Metals are good **conductors** of electricity. If more electrons are put in one end of a piece of metal, this will push electrons along the line. Imagine a line of people in a queue, each holding a ball. Each can hold only one ball. So if we give the person at one end another ball, they must pass their ball on down the line until the final person passes a ball out at the other end. This is a model of an electric current. In an electric current, electrons are passed along a line of atoms.

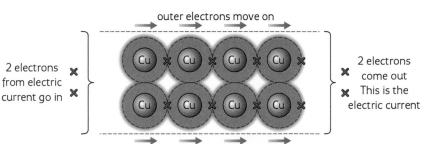

2 electrons from electric current go in

outer electrons move on

2 electrons come out
This is the electric current

Did you know?

The weight of gold in the human body (stored in the liver) is worth about 5 pence.

The uranium in your body would power a car for about 5 km.

- Metals are also good conductors of heat. If you heat one end of a piece of metal, the atoms at that end will vibrate. They will pass their vibration energy on to the next atoms, so conducting heat down the line.
- Metals shine because the outer electrons gain energy when light hits them. The electrons then release the energy again as light, making the metal shine.

Lead atom's mass = 207
Lead metal's density = 11 g/cm³

Aluminium atom's mass = 26
Aluminium metal's density = 2.7 g/cm³

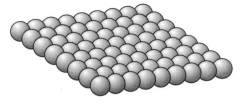

Both metals have similar giant metal structures, but the lead atom is 8 times heavier than the aluminium atom. The difference in atomic mass and the way the atoms are packed affects the density of the metal.

- The **density** of a metal depends not only upon the size and mass of its atoms, but also upon the way the atoms are packed. Some metals, such as lead, are very dense. Others, such as aluminium, are much less dense.

Upsetting the layers

Many of today's materials are mixtures of metals. When two or more different metals are mixed together, they form an **alloy**. But why mix metals together?

Atoms of a metal are in layers in giant metallic structures. If the atoms are all the same size, then the layers can move over each other. If you put in a metal with different sized atoms, it becomes more difficult to move one layer over another. This makes the metal harder.

If you heat up a metal, the atoms will vibrate out of their layers. If you allow it to cool slowly, the atoms will settle back into layers. But if you cool it very quickly, the atoms remain out of place, making the metal harder. For example, blacksmiths make use of this to make horseshoes harder.

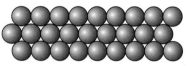

pure metal

alloy

Pure metal like copper. All atoms are the same size and can move over each other.

Add another metal to the copper and the properties change. Imagine tin is added: the tin atoms are a different size and this upsets the layers and prevents atoms moving. This makes the metal mixture or alloy harder.

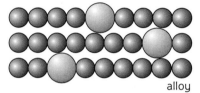

Metal giant structure

atoms vibrate

Vibrations pass along the line of atoms. This is called conduction of heat

heat

Atom vibrate more and need more space. The metal expands.

Questions

2 How do metals bond together?

3 How does the bonding help metals conduct electricity?

4 What is an alloy and why do chemists try to make alloys?

Covalent bonds

Objectives

This spread should help you to

- know that atoms can share electrons to make a covalent bond
- describe a covalent bond
- draw a diagram of a covalent bond

Covalent bonds

If an atom needs just one electron to complete its outer shell, one way it can do this is to attract an electron from another atom. Another way is to *share* an electron with another atom.

In atoms, electrons are found in pairs. In a chlorine atom's outer shell there are seven electrons: three pairs and a single electron. Two chlorine atoms can share their single electrons as a pair. This sharing of electrons is a **covalent bond**. The combined chlorine atoms are called a **molecule**.

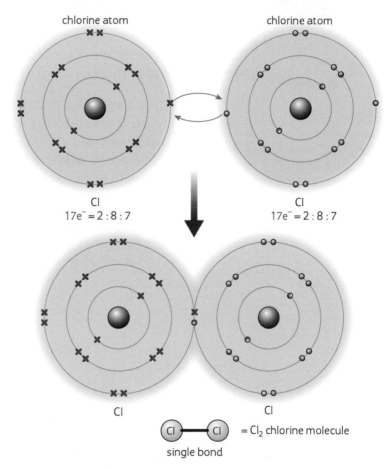

Quick tip

You can show the complete covalent bond with a line between the two atoms. A double bond has two lines ...

Covalent bond = sharing pairs of electrons. Each chlorine atom now has a full outer shell of eight electons.

Covalent compounds

In a covalent compound the atoms in each molecule are held strongly together by sharing electrons. There are only weak forces holding the molecules together.

Candle wax is a covalent solid. Its molecules are long chains of carbon and hydrogen atoms. The bonds between the atoms of carbon and hydrogen in each molecule are very strong, so to break these takes a lot of energy. Before the wax can burn,

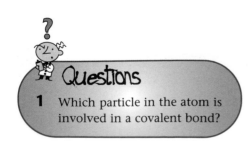

Questions

1 Which particle in the atom is involved in a covalent bond?

it needs to be melted and then vaporized into a gas. The solid wax consists of loosely held molecules. Heat easily breaks these weak attractive forces, and the wax molecules can flow and escape the surface of the liquid as a vapour.

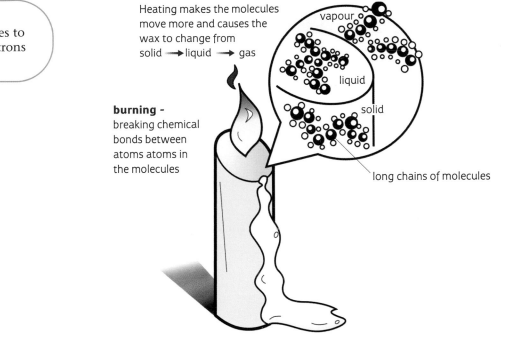

Heating makes the molecules move more and causes the wax to change from
solid ➝ liquid ➝ gas

vapour

liquid

solid

burning -
breaking chemical bonds between atoms atoms in the molecules

long chains of molecules

Candle wax is a solid made up of covalent molecules.

Because of these weak attractive forces between molecules, covalent molecular solids have low melting points. Many covalent compounds are liquids or gases at room temperature.

Also, because there are no electrically charged particles, covalent compounds do not conduct electricity even when liquid.

Some strong covalent substances are not made up of lots of small molecules. Instead they have many atoms joined together by covalent bonds into a giant structure.

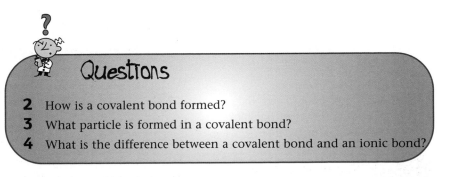

Questions

2 How is a covalent bond formed?

3 What particle is formed in a covalent bond?

4 What is the difference between a covalent bond and an ionic bond?

Covalent molecules (1)

Water and its bonds

A water molecule is made when two hydrogen atoms join with one oxygen atom.

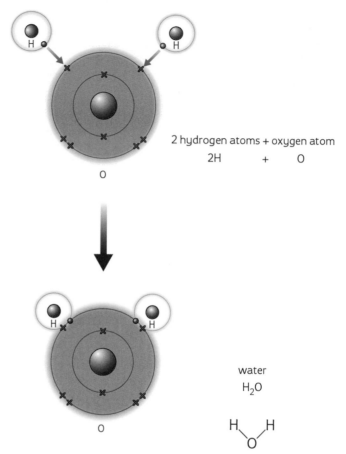

2 hydrogen atoms + oxygen atom

2H   +   O

water
H_2O

The formation of water.

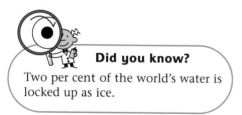

slightly
+

slightly
−

Water molecules have a slight electrostatic charge at each end. They attract each other. This attraction makes water molecules 'clump' together.

When oxygen shares electrons with hydrogen the attraction of the oxygen nucleus is very strong. This pulls the electrons away from the hydrogen, making that end of the molecule slightly positive. At the other end of the molecule are two pairs of electrons with their negative charge. This makes this end of the molecule of water slightly negative.

Water is called a polar molecule because it is slightly positive at one end and slightly negative at the other end.

Water molecules can now attract each other. These weak electrostatic bonds are what make water a liquid at room temperature and not a gas, like methane. (They are called hydrogen bonds and give water some of its strange properties.)

Hydrogen and oxygen

Hydrogen and oxygen are both non-metal gases and are 'made up' of molecules. Hydrogen molecules are composed of 2 hydrogen atoms.

Oxygen molecules are composed of 2 oxygen atoms.

When two atoms form a molecule it is called a diatomic molecule.

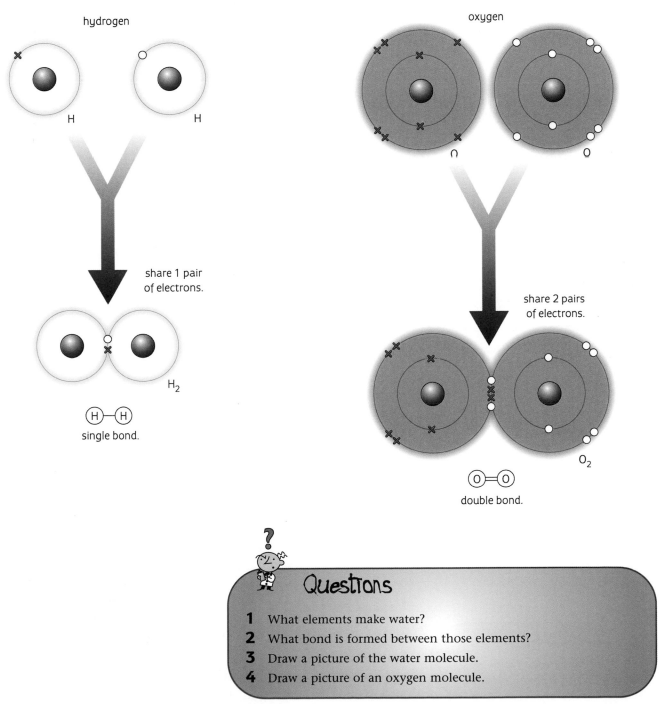

hydrogen

H

H

share 1 pair of electrons.

H₂

(H)—(H)
single bond.

oxygen

O

O

share 2 pairs of electrons.

O₂

(O)═(O)
double bond.

Questions

1 What elements make water?
2 What bond is formed between those elements?
3 Draw a picture of the water molecule.
4 Draw a picture of an oxygen molecule.

Covalent molecules (2)

Ammonia and its bonds

Nitrogen atoms have two electrons in the inner shell and five electrons in the outer shell. This means that nitrogen needs to gain three electrons to form the **octet** (eight electrons) in the outer shell. To gain three electrons would mean that the nitrogen would need to have a large attractive power. Another, easier, way is to share electrons with another atom, such as hydrogen. The result is ammonia (NH_3).

Ammonia is a colourless gas that is less dense than air. It is a gas, at room temperature. These properties are typical of a simple covalent substance. Weak attractive forces between the molecules mean that ammonia is a gas at low temperatures. Ammonia gas can dissolve easily in water.

A nitrogen atom.

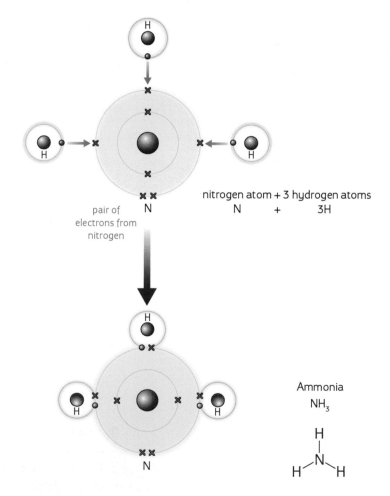

The formation of ammonia.

From planets to bacteria

Ammonia has had a varied career. About 4600 million years ago the atmosphere on Earth consisted of water vapour, carbon dioxide, nitrogen, methane, hydrogen, and ammonia.

The surfaces of Jupiter (left) and Saturn (right)

Today clouds of ammonia on Jupiter give the planet its varied colours. On Saturn it is so cold that ammonia can form tiny solid crystals that produce a haze. Ammonia freezes at $-78\,°C$.

On Earth ammonia has been shown to be one of the causes of bad smells. Bacteria commonly found on the skin break down body chemicals; among the products is ammonia. Babies often get nappy rash when bacteria break down urine to release ammonia.

Smell-less pigs in Ireland.

In farmyards animal urine is also broken down to release ammonia. In Ireland in 1991 they found that growing a variety of yucca plant reduced the smell because the plant took in ammonia and used it. Feeding yucca to farm animals also produced a pleasanter smelling waste. Most chemicals involved in the chemistry of life are covalently bonded, like ammonia.

Questions

2 Draw a diagram of the ammonia molecule and write down its formula.

3 Why is ammonia different from methane?

Covalent molecules (3)

Methane and its bonds

Carbon is a black, solid, non-metal element. Hydrogen is a colourless low-density gas. These two elements can combine to form a colourless flammable gas compound called methane.

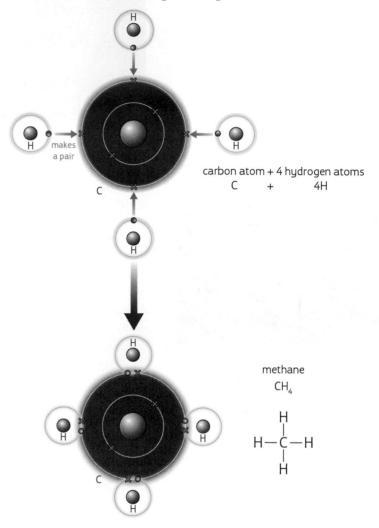

carbon atom + 4 hydrogen atoms

C   +   4H

methane
CH_4

The formation of methane.

Carbon has four electrons in its outer shell. These electrons are held tightly by the nucleus, so they are difficult to remove. To make a complete shell of eight electrons, carbon could *share* four electrons.

Hydrogen has one electron in its outer shell. Since this is the first shell, it would be full with two electrons. To make this a complete shell, hydrogen could share an electron.

If carbon shares an electron with each of four atoms of hydrogen, its outer shell is full. A molecule of methane is formed, which can be written as CH_4. Methane has four covalent bonds.

Both carbon and hydrogen will have complete shells by sharing electrons. There are no pairs of electrons on their own. The total number of protons in the molecule equals the total number of electrons. This molecule of methane is electrically **neutral**.

Hydrogen chloride

Another example of a covalent substance is hydrogen chloride.

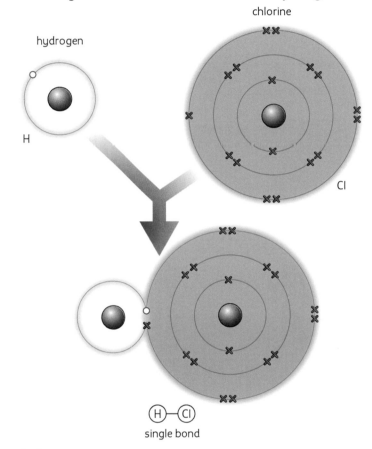

Dissolving

Some covalent gases like ammonia and hydrogen chloride are soluble in water. They form alkaline solutions. Other hydrogen halides, like hydrogen bromide will do the same.

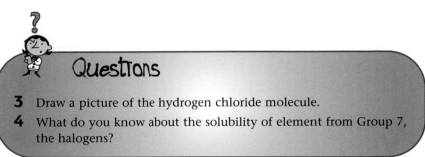

Questions

3 Draw a picture of the hydrogen chloride molecule.

4 What do you know about the solubility of element from Group 7, the halogens?

The periodic table: periods

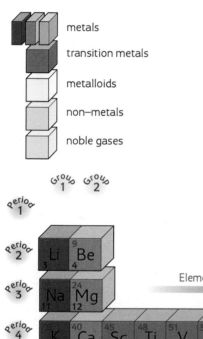

Objectives

This spread should help you to

- know what a period in the Periodic Table is
- describe how a period is developed
- demonstrate why the proton is important

metals

transition metals

metalloids

non–metals

noble gases

Problems with Mendeleev's table

Mendeleev arranged the elements by mass but he had to change the position of some elements. They did not fit the pattern of similar chemical reactions.

This changing of position made the pattern of elements right but was hard to explain. This was because no one knew about the atomic number. The atomic number is the number of protons in the atom. It was only in 1913 that Harold Moseley realized that the important key to an element's position in the periodic table was atomic number.

Periods in the modern periodic table

Imagine the periodic table as a town in which the elements live. The **period** is the street in which an element lives. The **group** is the address of the element in the street. Every element has a different atomic number. You could think of the atomic number as the telephone number of the element.

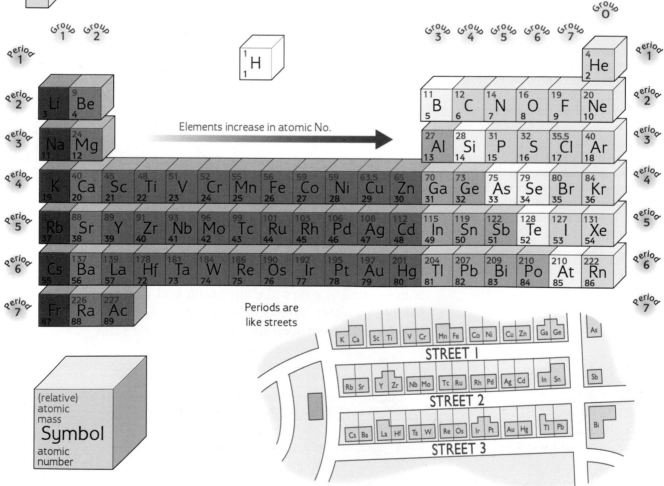

Elements increase in atomic No.

Periods are like streets

(relative) atomic mass

Symbol

atomic number

Members of a family can live in different streets in a town yet still be members of the same family. In the same way, two elements can both be in Group 1, say, but be in different periods. They cannot be in both the same group and the same period.

Patterns across a period

Using Period 2 as an example you can see a pattern in the change in the properties of elements as you move through the period (from left to right).

Remember!

Atoms can be represented by, for example:

atomic mass number $\rightarrow$
atomic number $\rightarrow$

$$^{23}_{11}Na$$

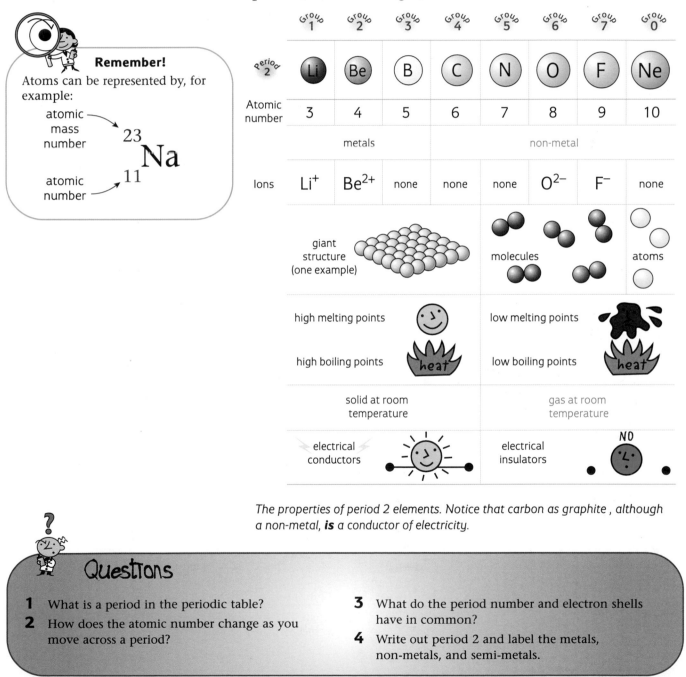

*The properties of period 2 elements. Notice that carbon as graphite , although a non-metal, **is** a conductor of electricity.*

Questions

1 What is a period in the periodic table?

2 How does the atomic number change as you move across a period?

3 What do the period number and electron shells have in common?

4 Write out period 2 and label the metals, non-metals, and semi-metals.

Period of change: Period 3

Atoms and ions: one trend across the period

Period 3 elements have three shells of electrons and the number of electrons in the third shell goes up one at a time across the period.

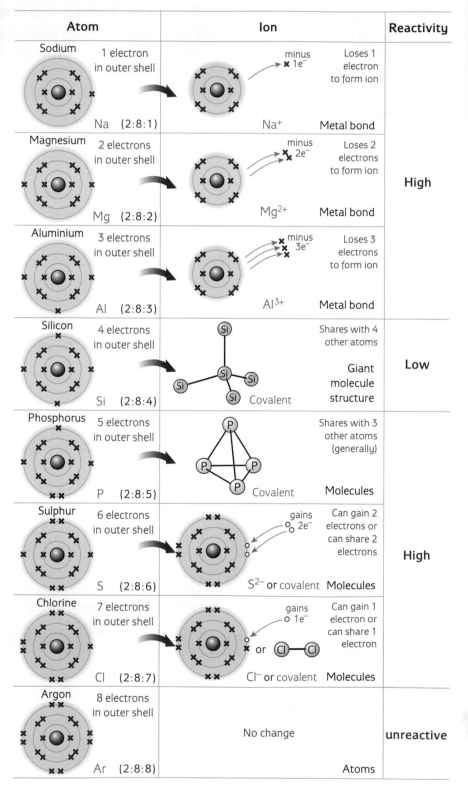

Atom	Ion	Reactivity
Sodium — 1 electron in outer shell — Na (2:8:1)	minus 1e⁻ — Loses 1 electron to form ion — Na⁺ — Metal bond	High
Magnesium — 2 electrons in outer shell — Mg (2:8:2)	minus 2e⁻ — Loses 2 electrons to form ion — Mg²⁺ — Metal bond	
Aluminium — 3 electrons in outer shell — Al (2:8:3)	minus 3e⁻ — Loses 3 electrons to form ion — Al³⁺ — Metal bond	
Silicon — 4 electrons in outer shell — Si (2:8:4)	Shares with 4 other atoms — Giant molecule structure — Covalent	Low
Phosphorus — 5 electrons in outer shell — P (2:8:5)	Shares with 3 other atoms (generally) — Molecules — Covalent	
Sulphur — 6 electrons in outer shell — S (2:8:6)	gains 2e⁻ — Can gain 2 electrons or can share 2 electrons — S²⁻ or covalent — Molecules	High
Chlorine — 7 electrons in outer shell — Cl (2:8:7)	gains 1e⁻ — Can gain 1 electron or can share 1 electron — or Cl—Cl — Cl⁻ or covalent — Molecules	
Argon — 8 electrons in outer shell — Ar (2:8:8)	No change — Atoms	unreactive

The reactivity of Period 3 elements

As you go across the period the number of electrons in the outer shell changes the way the atoms react. The left hand elements can lose electrons. The right hand elements, except argon, can gain electrons to form ionic bonds. They can also share electrons to form covalent bonds. As more electrons are involved, the reactivity gets lower. Sodium and chlorine have only one electron involved in any change to the outside shell, so they are very reactive. Silicon in the middle must share four electrons. It is not very reactive.

In the solid metal sodium the atoms are loosely packed together. This makes the metal soft and gives sodium a low melting and boiling point. As you move across the period the metals get harder until aluminium, which has the highest melting and boiling point and is the hardest metal in the period. The *element* with the highest melting point in the period is silicon.

Increasing atomic number ⟶

	Sodium	Magnesium	Aluminium	Silicon	Phosphorus	Sulphur	Chlorine	Argon
	Grey, very soft, shiny, solid, metal	Grey, soft shiny, solid, metal	Grey, hard, shiny, solid, metal	Dark grey, shiny, hard semi-metal	White, soft, waxy, solid, or red powder, non-metal	Yellow, soft, solid, non-metal	Pale green, gas, non-metal	Colourless, gas, non-metal
Melting Point	98 °C	649 °C	660 °C	1410 °C	44 °C	113 °C	− 101 °C	− 189 °C
Boiling Point	883 °C	1090 °C	2467 °C	2355 °C	277 °C	445 °C	− 34 °C	− 186 °C

You can see the same pattern for the non-metals, but this time working from the right and starting at argon. Argon is a noble gas and so is found as atoms. The atoms do not have a very strong attraction for each other so argon is a gas. Chlorine is found as molecules of two atoms. Again these molecules do not attract each other much so chlorine is a gas. By the time you get to silicon the atoms are sharing in a giant structure. This makes a solid that is hard. It has a high melting point because the bonds are very strong.

Silicon is like both metals and non-metals. It marks the change from metal to non-metal. It is sometimes called a **metalloid** or semi-metal.

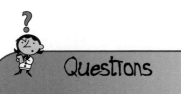

Questions

3 Why is silicon strange compared with magnesium and chlorine?

4 Draw a graph of the change in melting and boiling point. Why do you think they are different?

The periodic table: groups

We all belong to some group, like a family. If we look at the members of a family they have something in common. It might be a big nose or ears. We have all heard others say there's a family resemblance.

The periodic table is a huge collection of elements. It can be divided into families of elements that are alike. Mendeleev arranged them by atomic mass.

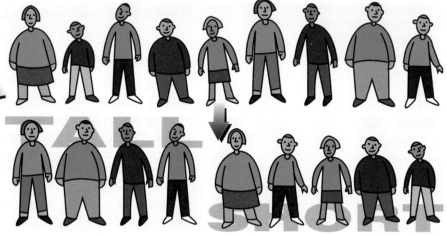

Picture a crowd of people in the school hall. To sort them, you could use height, mass, dress, hair colour, and so on. If you start by sorting them by height, suddenly other patterns appear, like mass, hand size, and foot size.

Mendeleev first lined the elements up in order of their atomic mass. Then he looked at the way the elements reacted. He found that he could divide the elements into vertical columns, so that all the elements in each column were very similar. They formed a family or **group**.

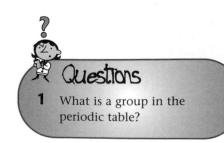

Questions

1 What is a group in the periodic table?

Electron shells

All the elements in a vertical group have the same number of electrons in the outer shell.

So the group number equals the number of electrons in the outer shell. That is why the elements in a group are so similar in their reactions. The elements in a group are similar but not exactly the same.

Patterns in groups

Group	Group 1 Group 2	Group 3 Group 4 Group 5 Group 6	Group 7	Group 0
Atoms in these:	• are reactive metals • form positive ions • get bigger as you go down the group • form small ions • are more reactive as you go down the group • Group I form hydroxides which dissolve in water to form alkaline solutions	• get more metallic as you go down the group • at the top of the group; prefer to share electrons • at the bottom of the group; react by losing electrons	• are reactive non-metals • form negative ions • get bigger as you go down the group • form big ions • are less reactive as you go down the group • has higher melting and boiling points as you go down the group.	• are unreactive • are all gases • do not form ions • have complete shells • get larger in size as you go down the group

Confusing?

Sometimes Group 0 is called Group 8!

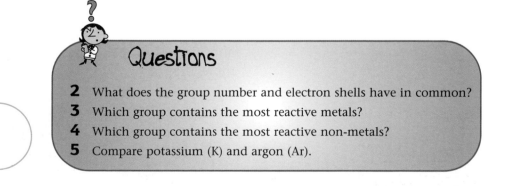

Questions

2 What does the group number and electron shells have in common?

3 Which group contains the most reactive metals?

4 Which group contains the most reactive non-metals?

5 Compare potassium (K) and argon (Ar).

8.20

Group 7: the halogens

Objectives

This spread should help you to

- name some of the elements in Group 7
- know the common reactions and physical properties of Group 7 elements
- describe what happens to the reactivity of the elements as you go down the group

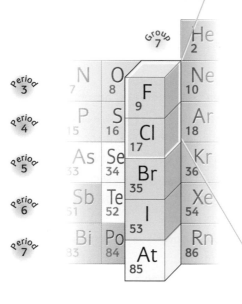

Atoms and ions

The elements in Group 7 are all non-metals.

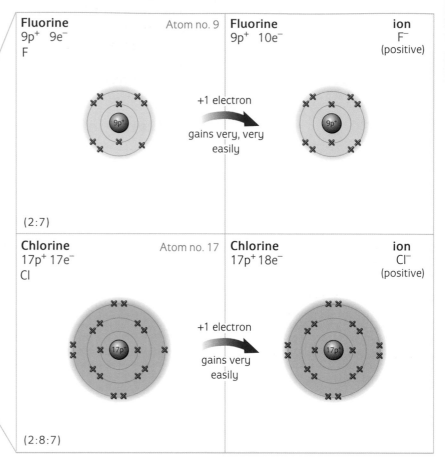

The Group 7 elements are very reactive non-metals. To complete the outer shell octet (8 electrons) they only need to gain one electron. The nucleus exerts a powerful attractive force. So a lone electron coming close to the halogen atom is pulled quickly into the outer shell. They form ionic salts. Halogens are poor conductors of heat and energy.

As an alternative the **halogen** atom can share an electron with another non-metal element. This means halogens can form molecules of two atoms.

Questions

1 What are the elements in group 7?
2 How do they change as you go down the group?

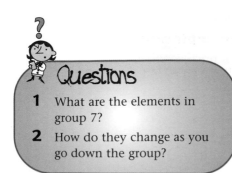

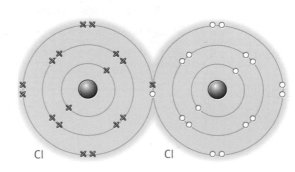

chlorine molecule

Cl_2
diatomic molecule
(2 atoms)

Reactivity of Group 7

Going down Group 7, the halogen atoms get larger and the positive pull gets weaker. This means the attraction, although still strong, is weaker for iodine atoms than for fluorine atoms. So iodine is less **reactive** than fluorine, chlorine, and bromine.

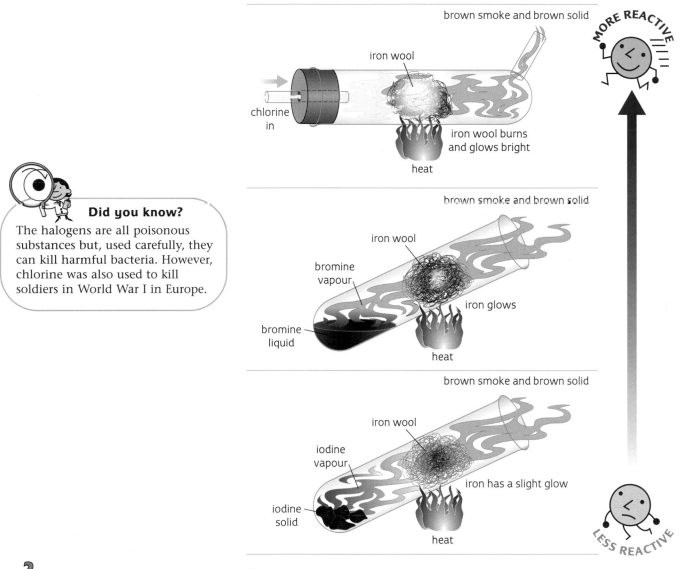

How the halogens react with iron.

Physical properties of the halogens

Group 7 element	Appearance/state	Melting point	Boiling point
fluorine	pale yellow gas	− 220 °C	− 188 °C
chlorine	pale green gas	− 101 °C	− 35 °C
bromine	red-brown liquid	− 7 °C	59 °C
iodine	brittle grey solid	114 °C	184 °C

Group 0: the noble gases

This spread should help you to

- name some of the elements in Group 0
- know the physical properties of the Group 0 elements
- describe the reactivity of the elements in Group 0

Atoms of Group 0 – the noble gases

The elements in Group 0 are all non-metals.

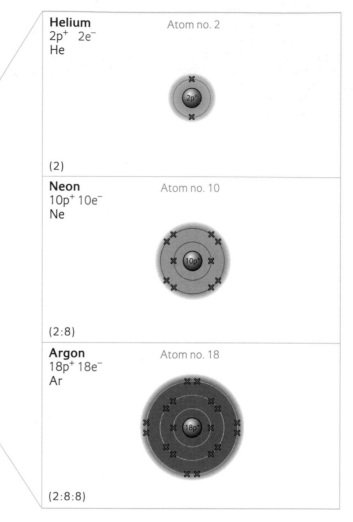

Helium
2p⁺ 2e⁻
He
Atom no. 2

(2)

Neon
10p⁺ 10e⁻
Ne
Atom no. 10

(2:8)

Argon
18p⁺ 18e⁻
Ar
Atom no. 18

(2:8:8)

Each atom has its outside shell full. It does not need to gain or lose any electrons. This means **noble gases** do not form bonds easily: they are unreactive. The atoms of the elements in Group 0 go around on their own.

Noble gas 'molecules' are monatomic (one atom).

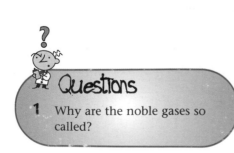

Questions

1 Why are the noble gases so called?

Because they do not need to lose or gain electrons, these elements do not form bonds with themselves either. They are called 'noble' for this reason.

Uses of noble gases

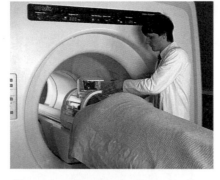

The magnet in a medical scanner is cooled by liquid helium.

Helium-oxygen breathing mixture protects against divers' 'bends'.

Helium is lighter that air and much safer than hydrogen.

Las Vegas is the 'neon' city.

Intensely bright Xenon arc lamps can be seen over great distances.

Krypton laser.

Questions

2 What is different about the outside electron shell of these elements compared to other elements?

3 Why do the noble gases not form compounds easily?

The alkali industry

Objectives

This spread should help you to

- know what the alkali industry is and why it is important
- describe how electrolysis is used in the alkali industry
- state some of the reactions that produce the products

People have been making glass, soap and paper for a long time.

Did you know?

Chlorine bleaches damp litmus paper.

Development of the alkali industry

The making of glass, soap, and paper are old industries. They each need 'soda'. This important compound is mostly sodium carbonate. It was either found naturally or made by changing common salt into soda. Ancient glass makers mixed sand, soda, and lime and heated them until they melted to form glass.

To make soap and paper the soda was heated with animal fats and plant oils. Finding the soda was difficult. Soda was an important trading material.

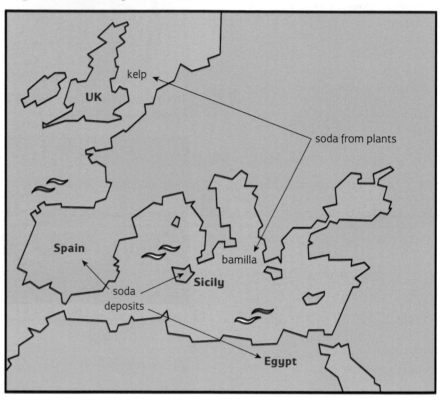

Soda came from various sources.

It was a dirty industry. In the early part of the nineteenth century Humphrey Davy (1778-1821) and Michael Faraday (1791-1867) used electrolysis to break down salt. By 1867 electrolysis was being used by industry to change common salt into sodium hydroxide.

The first factory making sodium hydroxide was set up at Runcorn in England because of all the rock salt found there.

Using electricity reduced the amount of heating and the amount of smoke. It was also more efficient. More soda could be produced from the same amount of salt. In 1863 only about 15% of the raw material became soap or bleaching powder but using electrolysis this more than doubled.

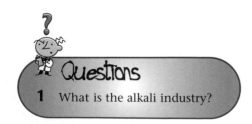

Questions

1 What is the alkali industry?

Cheshire was the first centre of the alkali industry.

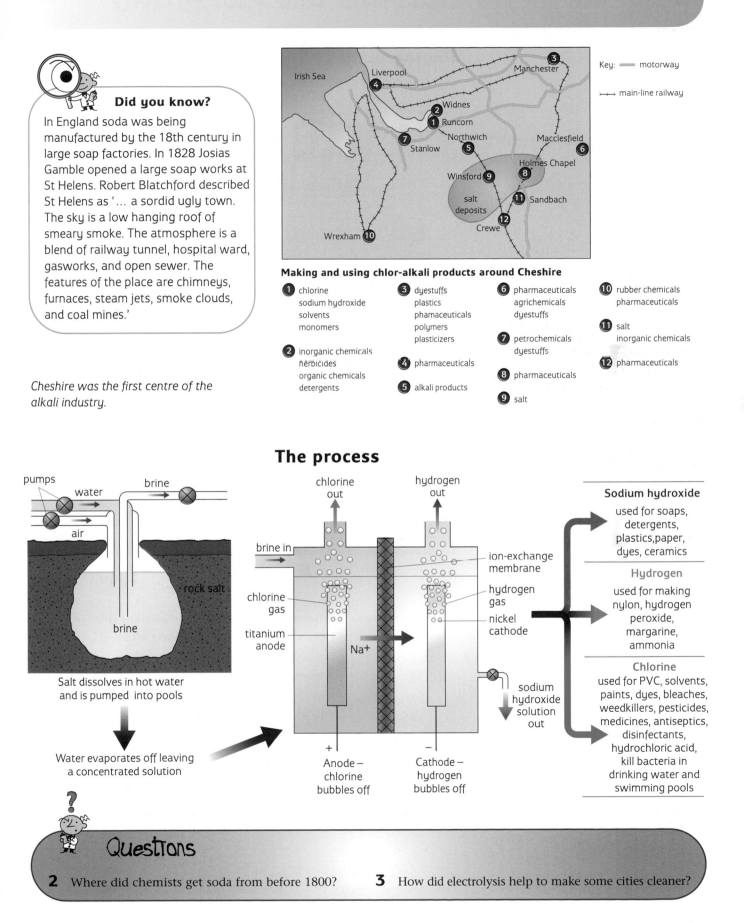

Making and using chlor-alkali products around Cheshire

1 chlorine
sodium hydroxide
solvents
monomers

2 inorganic chemicals
herbicides
organic chemicals
detergents

3 dyestuffs
plastics
phamaceuticals
polymers
plasticizers

4 pharmaceuticals

5 alkali products

6 pharmaceuticals
agrichemicals
dyestuffs

7 petrochemicals
dyestuffs

8 pharmaceuticals

9 salt

10 rubber chemicals
pharmaceuticals

11 salt
inorganic chemicals

12 pharmaceuticals

The process

Salt dissolves in hot water and is pumped into pools

Water evaporates off leaving a concentrated solution

Anode – chlorine bubbles off

Cathode – hydrogen bubbles off

Sodium hydroxide
used for soaps, detergents, plastics, paper, dyes, ceramics

Hydrogen
used for making nylon, hydrogen peroxide, margarine, ammonia

Chlorine
used for PVC, solvents, paints, dyes, bleaches, weedkillers, pesticides, medicines, antiseptics, disinfectants, hydrochloric acid, kill bacteria in drinking water and swimming pools

Questions

2 Where did chemists get soda from before 1800?

3 How did electrolysis help to make some cities cleaner?

Halogens and photography

Photography

A camera is a simple device, a light-tight box with a lens to focus the image on to light-sensitive film.

The black and white film is made up of grains or crystals of silver compounds. This is usually silver bromide ($AgBr$). These grains are set in gelatin, spread on a sheet of cellulose.

When light falls on the film, some of the silver bromide is reduced to silver.

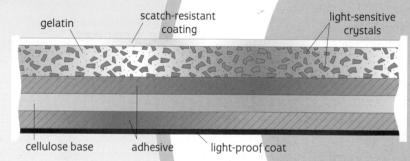

gelatin — scatch-resistant coating — light-sensitive crystals

cellulose base — adhesive — light-proof coat

The size of the grains containing the light-sensitive silver compound can be changed. On a slow film, one for a very bright day, the silver compound crystals are made fat and irregular. They have a small surface area, so the rate of reaction is slow.

To make a 'faster' film for dimmer days the silver compound crystals are made thinner and flatter. This increases the surface area. So more of the silver bromide is exposed to the light and even a little light will produce a detectable amount of silver.

light wave
hits silver ion

Ag
becomes silver atom

The silver atoms cannot be seen until developed

ISO 100

ISO 200

The speed of the film is shown on the box by the ISO (International Standards Organization) number, e.g. ISO 100 for a bright day, ISO 200 or ISO 400 for a dull day.

The negative needs to be developed and fixed. The fixer is sodium thiosulphate, which removes a pattern of unexposed silver compound, leaving black silver grains behind on the film as a negative image of the original scene.

Colour photography uses a film with a sandwich of three coloured dyes: red-sensitive, green-sensitive, and blue-sensitive, with the silver compound in the gelatin.

ISO 400

Light exposes the silver to form dark areas, and the coloured layers only allow certain types of colour through. When the film is developed, the three dyes produce the colour while the silver produces the image.

Much of the development of modern photography came from the work of George Eastman (1854–1932), who set up the Kodak company.

Talking point

Do you think digital cameras (electronic ones with no film) will replace film cameras?

Elements and symbols

States of matter

Just as words are made up of a combination of 26 letters, everything around us is made up of around 100 chemical elements in different combinations. These **elements** can be found at different temperatures in three different states: solid, liquid, and gas.

Solid elements: silver (Ag); sulphur (S)

Liquid elements: bromine (Br); mercury (Hg)   A gaseous element: chlorine (Cl)

Antoine Lavoisier (1743–1794) was the first to suggest the idea that we can change a substance like iron into a solid or a liquid or a gas: but it is still the same substance.

Conservation of matter

Lavoisier was good at experiments. Like John Dalton (1766–1844), he always weighed materials before and after an experiment. He discovered that the mass remained the same. Sometimes things appear to get lighter. But that's because a gas is given off that escapes. If you weigh the gas too, the mass is the same.

Lavoisier concluded that 'mass before' equals 'mass after': mass is **conserved**.

Chemical elements

The idea that matter can exist in three different **states** and the idea that matter is not created out of nothing made chemistry simpler. Lavoisier defined an **element** as a substance that could not be broken down into any other substance. Dalton was the first to describe an element as a substance made of only one kind of atom.

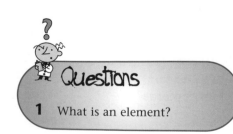

Questions

1   What is an element?

All the particles are the same = an element.

A selection of different particles = a mixture.

Particles of two different kinds joined to each other = a compound.

Did you know?

polonium: named in honour of Poland

krypton: a Greek word for 'hidden' or 'mysterious'

hydrogen: a Greek word meaning 'water maker'

oxygen: a Greek word meaning 'acid maker'

Symbols

Every element has a name and a shorthand symbol. Scientists have named elements after countries, people, and Greek or Latin words describing the element.

The symbol is generally the first letter and either the second or third letter in the name. But some elements have symbols that reveal an older name, for example:

- potassium, symbol **K** from its Latin name **Kalium**
- sodium, symbol **Na** from its Latin name **Natrium**.

Elements and symbols

Element	Symbol	Element	Symbol
sulphur	S	gold	Au
iron	Fe	lead	Pb
copper	Cu	aluminium	Al
tin	Sn	phosphorus	P

About four-fifths of the elements are metals. Metals have a number of properties in common:

1 they allow electricity and heat to pass through them easily – they are good conductors;
2 most are solids and have high melting points – except mercury;
3 most metals can be hammered into different shapes – they are malleable; they can also be pulled into thin wires – they are ductile.

Questions

2 What are the symbols for the following elements: gold, mercury, aluminium, iron?

3 Which elements have the symbols Cu, Si, O, Ca, Na?

4 Why is the conservation of mass so important?

Compounds and symbols

Objectives

This spread should help you to

- describe a compound as different from a mixture
- know the difference between physical and chemical change
- know a compound can be represented by symbols

Screwing the bits together did not produce the monster. Dr Frankenstein had to do something. He passed electricity from lightning through the body. This changed the mixture of body parts into a living thing.

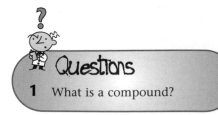

Questions

1 What is a compound?

Compounds and mixtures

A favourite theme of horror stories is the creation of a monster by a scientist. In the 18th century Mary Shelley wrote about an imaginary scientist called Dr Frankenstein, who created a monster from the different body parts of dead people.

In 1953 Stanley Miller (born 1930) mixed together hydrogen, methane, and ammonia and put them in a container with water. For a week he passed electricity through the mixture, just like lightning. At the end of the week he found he had made two of the chemicals most important to life – alanine and glycine.

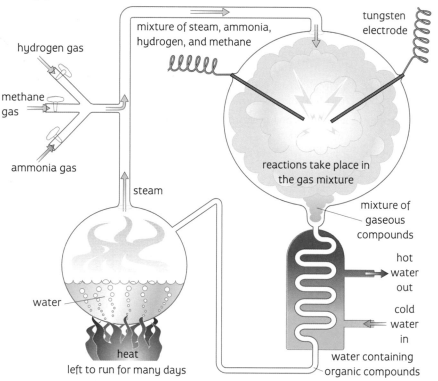

Stanley Miller's experiment to create the molecules of life: a modern attempt at the Frankenstein story.

The element alphabet

Just as we use the 26 letters of the alphabet to make words, scientists do the same with the elements. But they have to do something like burn, explode, or shake chemicals together. Elements can combine to make **compounds**. A compound is a combination of different elements. The 'alphabet' for compounds is the elements (there are around 100).

Combining elements

Hydrogen is a colourless gas. Oxygen is a colourless gas. They react together explosively to form the compound hydrogen oxide, or water, which is a colourless liquid.

Iron is a heavy metal that is magnetic. Sulphur is a light flour-like yellow powder. If you mix iron filings and sulphur you can easily separate them again using a magnet. But if you heat them, they form the compound iron sulphide. Iron sulphide is not magnetic. Iron sulphide is different from both iron and sulphur. A chemical change has occurred.

Symbols for compounds

Scientists use symbols for the elements. When they use combinations of elements to make compounds, they combine the symbols to represent the compound.

When a compound is made, it always has the same amount of each element. So water always has 2 atoms of hydrogen combined with 1 atom of oxygen. Iron sulphide always has 1 atom of iron combined with 1 atom of sulphur. In Stanley Miller's experiment each glycine molecule consists of 2 carbon atoms, 5 hydrogen atoms, 1 nitrogen atom, and 2 oxygen atoms.

If hydrogen and oxygen are mixed up, it is possible to separate them. The compound water is not easy to separate. The properties of the compound are different from the starting elements.

$$6\,H_2(g) \quad + \quad 3\,O_2(g) \longrightarrow 6\,H_2O(l)$$

REACTANTS		PRODUCTS
hydrogen gas molecules + oxygen gas molecules	mixture of atoms of hydrogen and oxygen	water molecules

Substance	Symbol	Property
hydrogen	H_2	colourless gas, light, explosive
oxygen	O_2	colourless gas, about the same mass as air
water	H_2O	colourless liquid, extinguishes fire

Questions

2 How is a compound different from a mixture?

3 Which requires a chemical reaction to make it – a compound or a mixture?

4 What is the chemical symbol for water and what elements are combined to make it?

Writing balanced equations

This spread should help you to

- know some chemical symbols to and how write an equation
- be able to write a word equation
- be able to write a balanced symbol equation

Writing chemical equations and making sure they are balanced is like a simple maths game. The rules are simple if you follow them in order.

Rule One

- know the compounds and elements involved in the reaction and write the word equation

Example 1

The reaction hydrochloric acid solution with sodium hydroxide solution.

hydrochloric acid + sodium hydroxide →
   sodium chloride + water

Example 2

The burning of magnesium metal in oxygen to form white solid magnesium oxide.

magnesium + oxygen → magnesium oxide

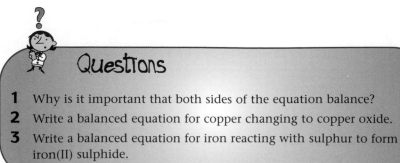

Questions

1 Why is it important that both sides of the equation balance?
2 Write a balanced equation for copper changing to copper oxide.
3 Write a balanced equation for iron reacting with sulphur to form iron(II) sulphide.

Rule Two

- What takes part in a chemical reaction must be accounted for so what element goes in must be there at the end. This makes sure there is no loss of mass or atoms.

As atoms are represented by chemical symbols each single symbol is an atom. More than one atom of the same element is represented by a number so in our first example:

Example 1

hydrochloric acid	+	sodium hydroxide	→	sodium chloride	+	water
HCl	+	NaOH	→	NaCl	+	H_2O

The equation is balanced.

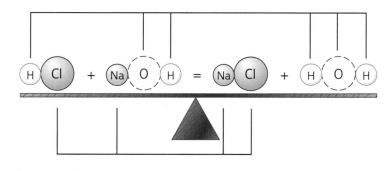

And remember...

You must remember these are in solution so you show that by using (aq) after the symbol and water is a liquid shown by (1).

$$HCl(aq) + NaOH(aq) → NaCl(aq) + H_2O(1)$$

Example 2

magnesium + oxygen → magnesium oxide

becomes

$$Mg(s) + O_2(g) → MgO(s)$$

but this leaves an oxygen over so you need two magnesium atoms to start with. This will then be:

$$2Mg(s) + O_2(g) → 2MgO(s)$$

The equation is balanced.

1 Arrange the following statements into 2 columns. In the left-hand column write the statements which are true of ELEMENTS and in the right-hand column write those which apply to COMPOUNDS:

- cannot be broken down into simpler substances
- can be broken down into simpler substances
- consist of different atoms in fixed proportions
- are made up of atoms with the same number of protons
- are represented by symbols
- are represented by formulae.

2 Copy and complete the following table.

Compound	Atoms present	Formula
water (hydrogen oxide)	2 hydrogen + 1 oxygen	
sodium oxide		Na_2O
magnesium oxide	1 magnesium + 1 oxygen	
aluminium oxide	2 aluminium + 3 oxygen	Al_2O_3
sodium chloride	1 sodium + 1 chlorine	
	1 magnesium + 1 chlorine	$MgCl_2$
aluminium chloride	1 aluminium + 3 chlorine	
sodium sulphate	2 sodium + 1 sulphur + 4 oxygen	Na_2SO_4
magnesium sulphate		$MgSO_4$
	2 aluminium + 3 sulphur + 12 oxygen	$Al_2(SO_4)_3$
		$MgCo_3$

3 Write down the names of the three major particles which make up atoms and state their relative masses, the charge on each and where they are located.

4 Boron consists of two isotopes which have the symbols $^{10}_5B$ and $^{11}_5B$. Both isotopes have the same atomic number (5), but one has a mass number of 10 and the other a mass number of 11.

a Draw diagrams of the two isotopes using p^+ to represent protons, n^0 to represent neutrons and e^- to show electrons.

b In every 10 atoms of boron 8 have a mass number of 11, and 2 have a mass number of 10.

Calculate:

i the total mass of 8 atoms of boron-11

ii the total mass of 2 atoms of boron-10

iii the total mass of 10 atoms of the isotope mixture

iv the average mass of 1 atom of boron.

5 Write a short paragraph to explain how the electrons in an atom of argon are arranged around the nucleus.

6 Copy and complete the following table for isotopes of some common elements:

Isotope	Name of element	Atomic number	Mass number	Number of p	Number of e	Number of n
$^{16}_8O$	oxygen	8	16	8	8	8
$^{18}_8O$						
$^{12}_6C$						
$^{13}_6C$						
$^{25}_{12}Mg$						
$^{26}_{12}Mg$						

7 The table below shows the structure of several particles:

Particle	Electrons	Protons	Neutrons
A	12	12	12
B	12	12	14
C	10	12	12
D	10	8	8
E	9	9	20

a Which three particles are neutral atoms?

b Which particle is a negative ion? What is the charge on this ion?

c Which particle is a positive ion? What is the charge on this ion?

d Use a table of 'electon shells' to identify the particles A to E.

8 Na^+ O_2 Al CH_4 N I^-

  a From the list above, select:

  i two atoms

  ii two molecules

  iii two ions.

  b What do the following symbols represent?

  i Na^+

  ii I^-

  c Name the compound made up from Na^+ and I^- ions, and write a formula for it.

9 This question is about the ionic bond formed between the metal lithium (atomic number 3) and the non-mental fluorine (atomic number 9).

  a How many electrons are there in a lithium atom? Draw a diagram to show its electron structure. (You can show the nucleus as a dark circle at the centre.)

  b How does a metal atom obtain a full outer shell of electrons?

  c Draw the structure of a lithium ion, and write a symbol for the ion.

  d How many electrons are there in a fluorine atom? Draw a diagram to show its electron structure.

  e How does a non-metal atom become a negative ion?

  f Draw the structure of a fluoride ion, and write a symbol for the ion.

  g Draw a diagram to show what happens when a lithium atom reacts with a fluorine atom.

  h Draw the arrangement of ions in the compound that forms when lithium and fluorine react together,

  i Write a name and a formula for the compound in part **h**.

10 a The electronic configuration of a neon atom is (2:8). What is special about the outer shell of a neon atom?

  b The electronic configuration of a calcium atom is (2:8:8:2). What must happen to a calcium atom for it to achieve a noble gas structure?

  c Draw a diagram of an oxygen atom, showing its eight protons (p), eight neutrons (n), and eight electrons (e).

  d What happens to the outer-shell electrons of a calcium atom, when it reacts with an oxygen atom?

  e Name the compound that is formed when calcium and oxygen react together. What type of bonding does it contain?

  f Write a formula for the compound in **e**.

11 a Write down a formula for each of the following:

  i a nitrate ion

  ii a sulphate ion

  iii a carbonate ion

  iv a hydroxide ion.

  b The metal strontium forms ions with the symbol Sr^{2+}. Write down the formula for each of the following:

  i strontium oxide

  ii strontium chloride

  iii strontium nitrate

  iv strontium sulphate.

12 Common salt (sodium chloride) exists as cubic crystals.

  a Describe or draw the arrangement of the sodium and chloride ions in a crystal.

  b What holds the ions together?

  c Why does salt have a very high melting point?

13 Write out the two sentences below, filling in the blanks with words from the following list:

  covalent ions hydrogen chlorine transfer share atoms electrons electrostatic molecules

  'Sodium chloride crystals consist of _____ formed by the _____ of electrons from sodium _____ to _____ atoms, held together by strong _____ forces.'

  'Methane gas consists of _____ made from carbon atoms and _____ atoms which _____ their _____ to make _____ bonds.'

14 Show how the electrons in the outer shells of two chlorine atoms are arranged when the atoms combine to form a molecule of chlorine.

15 a From a table of 'electron shells', write down the number of electrons there are in the outer shell (shell 2) of carbon, nitrogen, and oxygen.

  b Draw diagrams to show how the electrons are shared in the molecules of:

  i methane CH_4

  ii ammonia NH_3

  iii water H_2O.

Practice questions

16 Explain why the covalent substances methane and ammonia exist as gases.

17 a Why do water molecules have slight positive and negative charges at each end?

b Explain why water is a liquid, not a gas like methane or ammonia.

c Explain why the ionic substance sodium chloride dissolves in water.

18 In terms of the ways in which the atoms are bonded together, explain why metals are good conductors of electricity

19 Draw three columns and head them **Substance**, **Bonding**, and **State at room temperature** respectively.

Rearrange the following lists so that each substance has the correct bonding and state alongside it.

Substance: copper, methane. magnesium oxide, water, hydrogen chloride.

Bonding: ionic, covalent, giant covalent, metallic, covalent, hydrogen bonding.

State at room temperature: gas, liquid, solid, solid, solid.

20 Draw diagrams of the electron shell of chlorine atoms to show how they:

a gain electrons to become chlorine ions Cl⁻

b share electrons to become chlorine molecules Cl_2.

21 a Explain why the noble gases are so unreactive and exist as single atoms rather than as molecules.

b Give a use for each of three different noble gases.

22 Draw a table of 8 columns. Write 'sodium' at the top of the first column and the names of the other elements in Period 3 in the other seven. Fill in each column with:

a the number of electrons in the outer shell

b what happens to these electrons when the element combines

c whether the element is a metal or a non-metal

d the state of the element at room temperature

e how reactive the element is.

23 Give the chemical names of the following.

a $MgSO_4$ **b** NaCl **c** $CaCO_3$

d Na_2CO_3 **e** NaOH

24 This question is about elements from the families called: alkali metals, alkaline earth metals, transition metals, halogens, noble gases.

Element A is a soft, silvery metal which reacts violently in water.

Element B is a gas at room temperature. It reacts violently with other elements, without heating.

Element C is a gas that sinks in air. It does not react readily with any other element.

Element D is a hard solid at room temperature and forms coloured compounds.

Element E conducts electricity and reacts slowly with water. During the reaction its atoms each give up two electrons.

a Place the elements in their correct families. Give further element information about the position of the element within the family.

b Describe the outer shell of electrons for each element described above.

c How does the arrangement of electrons in their atoms make some elements very reactive and others unreactive?

d Name elements with fit descriptions A to E.

25 The diagrams below show a simple way of representing atomic particles. Copy and label each diagram correctly: 'uncharged atom', 'negative ion', 'positive ion', 'electron'.

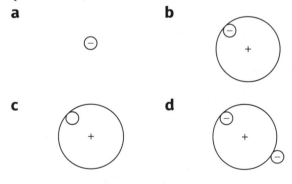

26 a Give the chemical symbols for:

i carbon

ii calcium

iii chlorine

iv copper.

b Sometimes the symbol O may be used, and sometimes the symbol O_2. When used in this way:

i what does the symbol O stand for?

ii what does the symbol O_2 stand for?

27 Many scientists contributed to the development of the modern Periodic Table. One of them was the Russian chemist Mendeleev. In 1869 he arranged the elements that were then known, in a table very similar to the one in use today. He realized that gaps should be left for elements that had not yet been discovered, and even went so far as to predict the properties of several of these elements. Rubidium is an alkali metal that lies below potassium in Group 1. Here is some data for Group 1:

Element	Proton number	Melting point (°C)	Boiling point (°C)	Chemical reactivity
Lithium	3	180	1330	quite reactive
Sodium	11	98	890	reactive
Potassium	19	64	760	very reactive
Rubidium	37	?	?	?
Caesium	55	29	690	violently reactive

a Using your knowledge of the Periodic Table, predict the missing data for rubidium.

b In a rubidium atom:

i how many electron shells are there?

ii how many electrons are there?

iii how many outer-shell electrons are there?

28 Write out the following passage, choosing the correct term from the words in brackets:

'The joining together of atoms or ions is called (**polymerisation/synthesis**). When iron is heated with sulphur, the two elements combine to form a new (**element/compound**) called (**iron sulphate/iron carbonate/iron(II) sulphide**). Decomposition is the (**joining/breaking**) up of a single (**element/compound**) into separate (**atoms/simpler products**) using heat, light or electricity to supply the (**force/energy**) needed to (**break/make new**) bonds. An example of thermal decomposition is the breaking up of (**green/yellow/black**) copper(II) carbonate on (**heating/cooling**) to form (**solid/liquid/gas**) carbon dioxide and (**black/blue**) copper(II) oxide.'

29 a Explain why chemical equations must 'balance'.

b Write out and balance equations for the following reactions:

i sodium burning in chlorine
$Na(s) + Cl_2(g) \rightarrow NaCl(s)$

ii magnesium burning in oxygen
$Mg(s) + O_2(g) \rightarrow MgO(s)$

iii sodium hydroxide solution neutralizing dilute sulphuric acid
$H_2SO_4(aq) + NaOH(aq) \rightarrow Na_2SO_4(aq) + H_2O(l)$

iv marble chips dissolving in dilute hydrochloric acid.
$CaCO_3(s) + HCl(aq) \rightarrow CaCl_2(aq) + CO_2(g) + H_2O(l)$

Key words

atom — the smallest particle of an element that can take part in a chemical reaction

atomic mass number — the sum of the number of protons and neutrons in an atom (AtNo. = No. of $P^+ + e^-$)

atomic number — the number of protons in an atom

bonds — when atoms join together by sharing electrons or losing/gaining electrons to form a charged atom

compound ions — a group of elements combined covalently but as a group lose or gain electrons to form a changed atom an ion

compounds — a substance made from the atoms of two or more elements chemically joined together

corrosion — metal reacts with oxygen to form an oxide

covalent bond — a bond formed between atoms by sharing electrons

electrons — small negative particle orbiting the nucleus of an atom, it has a mass small negative particle orbiting the nucleus of an atom, it has a mass $\frac{1}{1840}$ of an atom

element — a substance made up of only one type of atom, cannot be split up into simpler substances by chemical reactions

evaporation — when a liquids particles gain enough kinetic energy to escape the liquid as a vapour

group — a vertical column of elements in the periodic table

halogen — a non-metal element in group 7 of the periodic table

ion — when an atom loses an electron or gains an electron and loses a charge

ionic bond — a bond formed between atoms by losing or gaining electrons

ionic crystal — ions of different charges arranged in geometric clusters

isotopes — atoms of the same element having differing numbers of neutrons

kinetic energy — energy due to movement

metalloid — an element which has characteristics of a metal and non-metal

molecule — atoms chemically joined together with a covalent-bond by sharing electrons

neutron — a particle with no charge found in the nucleus of an atom, it has a mass of 1

noble gases — non-metal elements in group 0 of the periodic table

nucleus — the central part of an atom containing the protons and neutrons

octet (of electrons) — a shell of eight electrons

orbits — the shell in which electrons spin round the nucleus of an atom

period — a horizontal line of elements in the periodic table

products — the chemicals at the end of a reaction

protons — a positive particle found in the nucleus of an atom; it has a mass of 1

relative atomic mass (RAM) the mass of an element compared with the isotope of carbon 12

reactants the chemicals at the beginning of a reaction

states (of matter) matter is found in one of three states of matters, solid, liquid, gas. Solids melt to form a liquid, liquids boil to form a gas, a gas condenses to form a liquid, and a liquid freezes to form a solid

Exam-style questions

1. Commonly occurring ores include: malachite (copper(II) carbonate), tinstone (tin oxide), haematitie (iron(II) oxide), common salt (sodium chloride), and sylvine (potassium chloride).

   a. Explain what is meant by an ore.

   b. Why were gold and silver the earliest known metals?

   c. What metals were used 4000–6000 years ago in the Bronze Age? Why had these metals become available?

   d. Why was iron not generally used until the Iron Age began about 3000 years ago. How is iron extracted from its ores?

   e. The Group I metals, sodium and potassium, were not isolated until 1807. Why was this so and what did Sir Humphrey Davy use to extract them?

2. a. Copy out the following table and rearrange the rows to contain the correct information:

Element	State at room temperature	Colour	Relative atomic mass
chlorine	solid	grey	127
bromine	liquid	green	35.5
iodine	gas	red-brown	80

   b. To which group of the Periodic Table do these elements belong?

   c. How many electrons do they have in their outer shells?

   d. All atoms of chlorine contain 17 protons. Some contain 18 neutrons and others contain 20 neutrons.

      i. What is the mass number of each type of atom?

      ii. What is the symbol for each type?

      iii. What are the two types called?

3. Copy out the sentences, using a substance from the list to complete each one. (You may use a substance for more than one answer, or not at all.)

   Substances:

   argon   hydrogen
   carbon dioxide   water   sodium hydroxide
   dilute sulphuric acid   mercury   copper   steel

Sentences

   a. _____ turns universal indicator red.

   b. _____ has a pH of 7.

   c. _____ will neutralize sodium hydroxide solution.

   d. _____ is a strong alkali.

   e. Calcium carbonate fizzes when added to dilute hydrochloric acid because _____ is given off.

   f. _____ becomes rusty when exposed to air and water.

   g. _____ is an element with a boiling point below room temperature.

   h. _____ is a liquid metal used in thermometers.

   i. _____ is a gas composed of single atoms.

4. Dry air has the following composition:

   nitrogen 78%
   oxygen 21%
   argon 0.95%
   carbon dioxide 0.05%
   + other noble gases.

   a. Copy the pie chart and use the information above to label the correct sections.

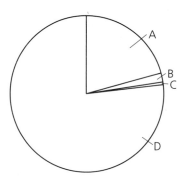

   b. Write a paragraph explaining how the gases in the air are separated using the terms: filtered; carbon dioxide and water removed, cooled, compressed, liquefied, fractionally distilled.

   c. Give two uses of each of:

      i. nitrogen

      ii. oxygen

      iii. argon.

5 a Explain what happens when oxygen combines with each of the substances listed below. In each case, write an equation for the reaction.

   i magnesium metal

   ii methane gas

   iii glucose in cells

b What energy change accompanies all three reactions?

c What is the term used for such energy changes?

6

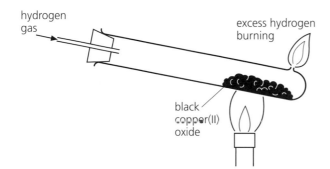

hydrogen gas

excess hydrogen burning

black copper(II) oxide

Using the apparatus shown in the diagram, a student weighed out some black copper(II) oxide and then heated it and passed hydrogen over it. The black powder changed to a reddish brown shiny solid. The student let it cool and weighed it again.

Results:

Mass of tube = 50.0 g

Mass of tube + copper(II) oxide = 58.0 g

Mass of tube + shiny solid = 56.4 g

a What was the shiny solid formed?

b What other product escaped as vapour?

c What was the mass of copper(II) oxide at the start?

d What was the mass of shiny solid formed?

e What was the mass lost?

f If the other product had been collected, what would its mass have been?

7 When magnesium ribbon is put into dilute sulphuric acid it dissolves rapidly and disappears, whilst a gas is given off as a vigorous fizzing. Magnesium will also dissolve in dilute ethanoic acid (vinegar), but more slowly, because this acid is much weaker than sulphuric acid.

a What is the difference between a strong acid and a weak acid?

b What is the gas given off in the reaction?

c What has happened to the magnesium?

d What would you see if you slowly evaporated the clear solution left when magnesium dissolves in dilute sulphuric acid?

e Write an equation in words and symbols for the reaction between magnesium and dilute sulphuric acid.

8 A piece of universal indicator paper dipped into a beaker of sodium hydroxide solution will turn dark blue (pH = 13–14). If dilute sulphuric acid is added, a little at a time, to the beaker, the mixture gets hot. Repeated testing with universal indicator paper will show that the mixture eventually becomes neutral. If this neutral solution is left to stand, it gradually evaporates and colourless crystals appear.

a What is the colour of the indicator paper when the solution is neutral and what is the pH value?

b What is the name of the crystals and what kind of substance are they?

c If 3.22 g of the crystals are gently heated, they change to a white powder which weighs only 1.42 g.

   i Calculate the loss in mass.

   ii Explain what is happening to cause this loss in mass.

9 Write out and complete the sentences **a**, **b**, **c**, and **d** using substances and pH values chosen from the following lists.

Substances: **caustic soda**   **oranges**   **battery acid**   **cream cleaners**

pH values: **1**   **3**   **8–9**   **13**

Sentences:

a _____ are often weakly alkaline with pH betwee _____.

b _____ control weak acids with pH around _____.

c _____ is a corrosive strong alkali with a pH of _____.

d _____ is a strong acid with a pH of _____.

10 Ammonia is made from nitrogen and hydrogen gases. The equation for the reaction is:

$$N_2(g) + 3H_2(g) \overset{Fe}{\rightleftharpoons} 2NH_3(g)$$

a Where does the nitrogen come from?

b How is the hydrogen produced?

c What does the symbol $\rightleftharpoons$ tell you about the reaction?

d What is the catalyst used in the reaction?

e Much of the ammonia produced by the process is reacted with nitric acid (HNO_3) to form the fertilizer ammonium nitrate. Write an equation for the reaction of ammonia with nitric acid.

f Give another important use of ammonium nitrate.

11 A student was investigating the rate of the reaction between calcium carbonate and dilute hydrochloric acid. She weighed out 10 g of small lumps of calcium carbonate and added them to some acid in a conical flask which was placed on a top-pan balance.

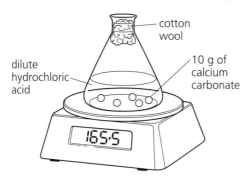

cotton wool

dilute hydrochloric acid

10 g of calcium carbonate

165·5

She noted the total mass which was 165.5 g. After one minute she noted that the mass had fallen to 163.7 g and noted the difference. She continued to note the loss in mass every minute until the fizzing in the flask stopped and there was no further loss in mass.

Her results were:

Time in minutes	1	2	3	4	5
Loss in mass (g)		2.8	3.4	3.8	4.05
Time in minutes	6	7	8	9	10
Loss in mass (g)	4.25	4.35	4.4	4.4	4.4

a What was the loss in mass in the first minute?

b What caused the loss in mass?

c Draw a graph to show how the loss in mass varies with time.

d Sketch on your graph paper the curves you would expect if the student had used:

i larger lumps of calcium carbonate

ii the same size lumps but hot acid in the flask.

e State two of the things the student should have kept the same in each experiment.

12 The following questions are about hydrocarbons.

a How are they obtained?

b What two elements are present in their molecules?

c What two products are formed when hydrocarbons burn in air?

d How is the boiling point of a hydrocarbon related to the length of its carbon chain?

e Write an equation for the burning of a hydrocarbon in the air.

f Long chain hydrocarbons are often subjected to the process of cracking.

i What is cracking?

ii Why is it done?

iii What kind of molecule is produced during cracking?

13 Explain in one or two sentences what is meant by each of the following:

a an exothermic reaction

b cracking

c a plastic

d a catalyst

e neutralization

14 The diagram below represents a cross-section through some rock layers.

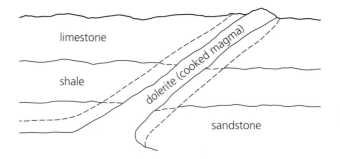

limestone

shale

dolerite (cooked magma)

sandstone

a Copy the diagram and mark or colour in areas which contain:

i igneous rock

ii sedimentary rock

iii metamorphic rock.

b Shale is changed by heat into a rock called hornfels.

i Mark with an H where hornfels might be found.

ii Mark with an M where marble might be found.

iii Mark with a Q where quartzite might be found.

15 The diagrams below show two igneous rocks in close-up:

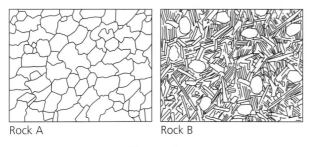

Rock A   Rock B

0 _____ 1 cm

a Which of the two igneous rocks cooled most quickly? Give reasons for your answer.

b What caused the round holes in rock N?

c Which of the two rocks is most likely to have solidified underground? Give reasons for your answer.

16 What is the relative formula mass of:

a sulphuric acid (H_2SO_4)?

b hydrochloric acid (HCl)?

c copper oxide (CuO)?

d water (H_2O)?

e sodium chloride (NaCl)?

f methane (CH_4)?

17 Calculate the % of the following elements:

a hydrogen in methane (CH_4)

b nitrogen in ammonia (NH_3)

c sodium in sodium hydroxide (NaOH)

d calcium in calcium carbonate ($CaCO_3$)

18 Draw diagrams to show how the electrons are shared in the following molecules:

a fluorine, F_2

b water, H_2O

c methane, CH_4

d trichloromethane, $CHCl_3$

e oxygen, O_2

f hydrogen sulphide, H_2S.

Draw the shapes of molecules **a**, **b** and **e**.

19 a An oxygen molecule is represented as O=O. What does the double line mean? How many electrons from each atom take part in bonding?

b A molecule of carbon dioxide (CO_2) can be drawn as O=C=O. Draw a diagram to show how the electrons are shared in the molecule.

20 The statements below are about metals and non-metals. Say whether each is true or false. (If false, give a reason.)

a All metals conduct electricity.

b All metals are solid at room temperature.

c Non-metals are good conductors of heat but poor conductors of electricity.

d Many non-metals are gases at room temperature.

e Most metals are brittle and break when hammered.

f Most non-metals are ductile.

g There are about four times as many metals as non-metals.

21 For each of the six elements aluminium (Al), boron (B), nitrogen (N), oxygen (O), phosphorus (P), sulphur (S) write down:

a the period of the Periodic Table to which it belongs

b its group number in the Periodic Table

c its proton number (atomic number)

d the number of electrons in one atom

e its electronic configuration

f the number of outer-shell electrons in one atom.

Which of the above elements would you expect to have similar properties? Why?

22 Read the following passage about the physical properties of metals.

Elements are divided into metals and non-metals. All metals are electrical conductors. Many of them have a high density and they are usually ductile and malleable. All these properties influence the way the metals are used.

a Explain the meaning of the words underlined.

b Copper is ductile. How is this property useful in everyday life?

c Aluminium is hammered and bent to make large structures for use in ships and aeroplanes. What property is important in the shaping of this metal?

d Name one metal that has a low density.

e Add the correct word: *Metals are good conductors of _____ and electricity.*

f Name one other physical property of metals and give two examples of how this property is useful.

23 a Copy this diagram and complete it by writing in:
i the common names
ii the chemical formulae.

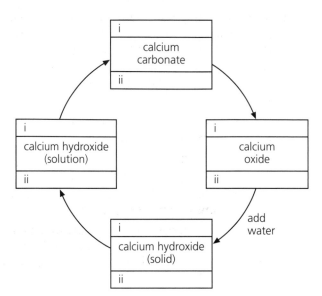

b Beside each arrow say how the change would be carried out. One example is shown.

c Give three reasons why limestone is an important raw material.

24 Limestone is calcium carbonate, $CaCO_3$. When limestone is heated, this chemical change occurs:

$$CaCO_3(s) \rightarrow CaO(s) + CO_2(g)$$

(Ca = 40, C = 12, O = 16)

a Write a word equation for the chemical change.

b i What mass of calcium oxide is obtained from the thermal decomposition of 50 g of calcium carbonate?

ii What mass of carbon dioxide would be given off at the same time?

25 Below are ten descriptions of a gas. Which of these describe the gas carbon dioxide?

a Colourless

b Given out during photosynthesis

c Turns lime water milky

d Burns in air

e Insoluble in water

f Heavier than air

g Has the formula CO_2

h Used up in burning carbon compounds

i Has no smell

j Is found in air

k A product of burning fossil fuels

l Forms a weak acid when it dissolves in water

26 Sodium hydrogen carbonate is often called sodium bicarbonate or bicarbonate of soda. Its formula is $NaHCO_3$. When heated it gives off a gas. It is used in baking soda, baking powder and indigestion tablets.

a Name the gas given off when bicarbonate of soda is heated. (Hint: it is also given off when limestone is heated!)

b Explain why the compound is used for baking.

c Why is sodium *carbonate* no use for baking?

d Hydrogen carbonates react like carbonates with acids. What products will be formed when sodium hydrogen carbonate reacts with hydrochloric acid?

e Write a balanced equation for this reaction.

f Explain why sodium hydrogen carbonate is used in indigestion tablets.

27 Catalytic converters are fitted to all new cars to reduce pollution caused by hydrocarbons, carbon monoxide and oxides of nitrogen in the exhaust gas.

a What are the main dangers associated with each of these pollutants?

b What is meant by a catalytic reaction?

c In one of the catalytic reactions nitrogen monoxide (NO) reacts with carbon monoxide to form nitrogen and carbon dioxide. Write a balanced equation for this reaction.

d What environmental problem is *not* solved by the use of catalytic converters?

e Why is the level of ozone at ground level increasing? Is this a good or a bad thing? Why?

28 Copy and complete the following paragraph:

Air is a _____ of different gases. 99% of it consists of the two elements _____ and _____. One of these, _____, is needed for respiration, which is the process by which living things obtain the _____ they need. The two elements above can be _____ from liquid air by _____ _____, because they have different _____ _____. Much of the _____ obtained is used to make nitric acid and fertilizers. Some of the remaining 1% of air consists of two compounds, _____ and _____. One of these is important because it is taken in by plants, in the presence of _____, to form _____. The rest of the air is made up of elements called the _____. These are all members of Group _____ of the Periodic Table.

29 The mixture of gases we call air developed over millions of years from the gas that burst from volcanoes.

a Most of the volcanic gas consisted of water vapour. But now there is only a tiny percentage of this in air. Why?

b The volcanic gas contained a large percentage of carbon dioxide. Where did most of this go?

c The volcanic gas also contained hydrogen chloride. Why is there none of this gas in air?

d Hydrogen is also absent from air, even though it was a constituent of volcanic gas. Where has it gone to?

e Which important gas in air was not present in the volcanic gas? Name the process that produced this gas over millions of years.

f Which gas makes up approximately 78% of the air?

g Only one gas in the mixture will allow things to burn in it. Which gas is this?

h How are the gases in the mixture separated from each other, in industry?

i Which noble gas is present in the greatest amount in air?

j Which gas containing sulphur is a major cause of air pollution?

k Name two other gases which contribute to air pollution.

l Name one substance which is not a gas but which also pollutes the air.

30 The manufacture of ammonia and nitric acid are both very important industrial processes.

A Ammonia

a Name the raw materials used.

b Which two gases react together?

c Why are the two gases scrubbed?

d Why is the mixture passed over iron?

e What happens to the *unreacted* nitrogen and hydrogen?

f Why is the manufactured ammonia stored at high pressure?

B Nitric acid

a Name the raw materials used.

b Which chemicals react together to form nitric acid?

c What would happen if the gauze containing platinum and rhodium was removed?

d Why must the chemical plant be constantly checked for leaks?

31 Ammonium compounds and nitrates are of great importance as fertilizers.

a Why do these compounds help plant growth?

b Name one *natural* fertilizer.

c Name two compounds containing nitrogen which are manufactured for use as fertilizers. Write the chemical formulae for these compounds.

d Name two elements other than nitrogen which plants need, and explain their importance to the plants.

e Why are some fertilizers not suitable for quick-growing vegetables like lettuce?

f Some fertilizers are acidic. What is usually added to soils to correct the level of acidity?

g Land which is intensively farmed needs regular applications of fertilizer. Explain why.

h Fertilizers obviously have advantages. But many people are worried about the increasing use of fertilizers, especially nitrates, by farmers. Can you suggest why?

32 Five solutions A to E were tested with universal indicator solution, to find their pH. The results are shown below.

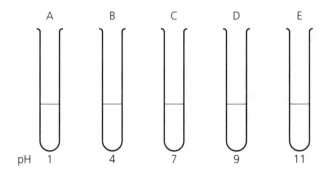

a What colour would each solution be?

b Which solution is:

i neutral?

ii strongly acidic?

iii weakly acidic?

iv strongly alkaline?

c The five solutions were known to be sodium chloride, sulphuric acid, ammonia solution, sodium hydroxide, and ethanoic acid. Now identify each of the solutions A to E.

Multi-choice questions

Module 5

1 Which of John Dalton's ideas about atoms was not entirely correct?

A Matter is made up of small particles called atoms.

B Atoms cannot be destroyed or created.

C Atoms of a particular element are all exactly alike and different from the atoms of another element.

D When atoms combine, whole numbers of atoms combine.

2 Which statement about elements is wrong?

A Elements cannot be broken down into simpler substances.

B Elements consist of atoms with the same atomic number.

C Elements often consist of molecules.

D Elements are all solids at room temperature.

3 Which of the following properties applies to most non-metals?

A Good conductors of electricity.

B Have low melting and boiling points.

C Shiny when polished.

D Malleable and ductile.

4 Which of the four elements is the most reactive non-metal?

A Fluorine

B Potassium

C Oxygen

D Chlorine.

5 Aluminium is used to make drinks cans. The following property makes it suitable for this:

A it can be recycled

B it is not corroded by acids

C it has a low density

D it is shiny and attractive

6 Carbon, aluminium oxide and iron(III) oxide are mixed. The mixture is lit. What is reduced?

A both aluminium oxide and iron(III) oxide

B carbon dioxide from the air

C iron(III) oxide only

D aluminium oxide only

7 Nickel is between iron and copper in the reactivity series. Which of the following metals will react with nickel(II) oxide?

A iron only

B aluminium and iron

C aluminium and copper

D copper only

8 Part of the reactivity series is shown below:

↑ zinc

tin

lead

silver

In which of the following mixtures will there be no reaction?

A lead with tin chloride solution

B tin with lead nitrate solution

C tin with silver nitrate solution

D zinc with tin chloride solution

9 Aqueous solutions of P and Q are mixed. The result is a solution with pH 7. Which could be the pH values of solutions P and Q?

	pH of solution P	pH of solution Q
A	3	5
B	3	12
C	7	11
D	8	13

10 Which of the following forms an acidic solution when dissolved in water?

A oxygen

B limestone

C sulphur dioxide

D nitrogen

Module 6

11 Which of the following processes does not affect the amount of carbon dioxide in the air?

A The burning of fossil fuels.

B The respiration of plants and animals.

C Photosynthesis.

D The action of de-nitrifying bacteria.

12 Which two gases are the main product of the combustion of petrol in a car engine?

A Water vapour and carbon monoxide.

B Hydrogen oxide and carbon dioxide.

C Carbon dioxide and carbon monoxide.

D Carbon dioxide and nitrogen oxides.

13 Which of the following are correct statements about hydrocarbons?

A They consist of carbon and hydrogen only.

B They are only found in oil.

C They all burn to form carbon dioxide and water.

D They react immediately with bromine.

14 Which statement about the gas methane is false?

A Its formula is CH_4.

B It contains only single bonds.

C It is colourless.

D It is a liquid at room temperature.

15 What is the term used for the formation of shorter chain hydrocarbons from longer ones?

A Fractional distillation

B Condensation

C Refining

D Cracking.

16 What is the main substance that makes up natural gas?

A kerosene

B propane

C methane

D ethene

17 The fractional distillation of crude oil gives the following products. Which one has the lowest boiling point?

A kerosene

B bitumen

C naphtha

D gasoline (petrol)

18 One of the following is *not* a fuel. Which one?

A hydrogen

B oil

C oxygen

D coal

19 Which substance produced when fossil fuels are burned does *not* cause damage to limestone buildings?

A nitrogen oxides

B carbon dioxide

C carbon monoxide

D sulphur dioxide

20 Which of the following results in more acid rain in the atmosphere?

A burning fossil fuels

B destruction of the ozone layer

C deforestation

D excessive use of pesticides

How to revise

There is no one method of revising that works for everyone. It is therefore important to discover the approach that suits you best. These guidelines may help you.

Give yourself plenty of time There are very few people who can revise everything 'the night before' and still do well in an examination the next day. You need to plan your revision to begin several weeks before the examinations start.

Plan your revision timetable Draw up a revision timetable well before the examinations start. Once you have done this, follow it – don't be sidetracked. Stick your timetable somewhere prominent where you will keep seeing it – or better still put several around your home!

Relax You will be working very hard revising. It is as important to give yourself some free time to relax as it is to work. So build some leisure time into your revision timetable.

Ask others Friends, relatives, and teachers will be happy to help if you ask them. Don't just give up on something that is causing you a problem. And don't forget your parents too!

Find a quiet corner Find the conditions in which you can revise most efficiently. Many people think they can revise in a noisy, busy atmosphere – most cannot! And don't try to revise in front of the television. Revision in a distracting environment is very inefficient.

Use routemaps or checklists Use routemaps, checklists, or other listing devices to help you work your way logically through the material. When you have completed a topic, tick it off. Tick off topics you already feel confident about. That way you won't waste time revising unnecessarily.

Make short notes and use colours As you read through your work or your textbooks, make brief notes of the key ideas and facts as you go along. But be sure to concentrate on understanding the ideas rather than just memorizing the facts. Use colours and highlighters to help you.

Practise answering questions As you finish revising each topic, try answering some questions. At first you may need to refer to your notes or textbooks. As you gain confidence you will be able to attempt questions unaided, just as you will in the exam.

Give yourself a break When you are revising, work for perhaps an hour, then reward yourself with a short break of 10 to 15 minutes while you do something different. Look out the window, stretch your legs, have a soft or hot drink. But when your 10 or 15 minutes are up, get back to work!

Success in examinations

Most people become a bit nervous about an important examination. If you have done most of your work consistently for two years and revised effectively, the following steps should help you to minimize anxiety and ensure that your examination results reflect all your hard work.

Be prepared Make sure you have everything you need ready the night before, including pens, pencils, ruler, and calculator. Check that you have anything else required well in advance.

Read carefully Before you start, spend a few minutes reading the paper all the way through. Make sure you know exactly what you have to do.

Plan your time Work out how much time you should spend on each question, based on how many marks it has. Allow yourself a few minutes at the end of the exam to check through your work.

Answer the question! When you are ready to start a question, read through it again carefully to make sure it really does say what you think it says. Follow the instructions to the letter: you will get marks for answering the question but not for giving other information about the subject.

Present your work clearly Write as clearly as you possibly can in the time available and think through what you are going to write before you begin writing. Draw diagrams clearly and simply, using single lines where appropriate. Label your diagrams and make sure the label lines point exactly to the relevant places. The examiner will be trying to award you marks – make it as easy for him or her to do so!

Keep calm!!! If you find a question you have no idea about, don't panic! Breathe slowly and deeply and have another look. It's likely that if you stay calm and think clearly, the question will start to make more sense, or at least you may be able to answer part of it. If not, then don't agonize about it – concentrate first on the questions you can answer.

KEY

Mass number A	H	
Atomic number (proton number) Z	Hydrogen	1

1	2											3	4	5	6	7	0
																	4 **He** Helium 2
7 **Li** Lithium 3	9 **Be** Beryllium 4											11 **B** Boron 5	12 **C** Carbon 6	14 **N** Nitrogen 7	16 **O** Oxygen 8	19 **F** Fluorine 9	20 **Ne** Neon 10
23 **Na** Sodium 11	24 **Mg** Magnesium 12											27 **Al** Aluminium 13	28 **Si** Silicon 14	31 **P** Phosphorus 15	32 **S** Sulphur 16	35 **Cl** Chlorine 17	40 **Ar** Argon 18
39 **K** Potassium 19	40 **Ca** Calcium 20	45 **Sc** Scandium 21	48 **Ti** Titanium 22	51 **V** Vanadium 23	52 **Cr** Chromium 24	55 **Mn** Manganese 25	56 **Fe** Iron 26	59 **Co** Cobalt 27	59 **Ni** Nickel 28	63 **Cu** Copper 29	64 **Zn** Zinc 30	70 **Ga** Gallium 31	73 **Ge** Germanium 32	75 **As** Arsenic 33	79 **Se** Selenium 34	80 **Br** Bromine 35	84 **Kr** Krypton 36
85 **Rb** Rubidium 37	88 **Sr** Strontium 38	89 **Y** Yttrium 39	91 **Zr** Zirconium 40	93 **Nb** Niobium 41	96 **Mo** Molybdenum 42	**Tc** Technetium 43	101 **Ru** Ruthenium 44	103 **Rh** Rhodium 45	106 **Pd** Palladium 46	108 **Ag** Silver 47	112 **Cd** Cadmium 48	115 **In** Indium 49	119 **Sn** Tin 50	122 **Sb** Antimony 51	128 **Te** Tellurium 52	127 **I** Iodine 53	131 **Xe** Xenon 54
133 **Cs** Caesium 55	137 **Ba** Barium 56	139 **La** Lanthanum 57	178 **Hf** Hafnium 72	181 **Ta** Tantalum 73	184 **W** Tungsten 74	186 **Re** Rhenium 75	190 **Os** Osmium 76	192 **Ir** Iridium 77	195 **Pt** Platinum 78	197 **Au** Gold 79	201 **Hg** Mercury 80	204 **Tl** Thallium 81	207 **Pb** Lead 82	209 **Bi** Bismuth 83	**Po** Polonium 84	**At** Astatine 85	**Rn** Radon 86
Fr Francium 87	226 **Ra** Radium 88	227 **Ac** Actinium 89															

Elements 58–71 and 90–103 have been omitted.

The value used for mass number is normally that of the commonest isotope, e.g. ^{35}Cl not ^{37}Cl.
Bromine is approximately equal proportions of ^{79}Br and ^{81}Br.

Reactivity series of metals

potassium
sodium
calcium
magnesium
aluminium
carbon
zinc
iron
tin
lead
hydrogen
copper
silver
gold
platinum

MOST REACTIVE

LEAST REACTIVE

(elements in italics, though non-metals, have been included for comparison).

Formulae of some common ions

| Positive ions | | Negative ions | |
Name	Formula	Name	Formula
hydrogen	H^+	chloride	Cl^-
sodium	Na^+	bromide	Br^-
silver	Ag^+	fluoride	F^-
potassium	K^+	iodide	I^-
lithium	Li^+	hydroxide	OH^-
ammonium	NH_4^+	nitrate	NO_3^+
barium	Ba^{2+}	oxide	O^{2-}
calcium	Ca^{2+}	sulphide	S^{2-}
copper(II)	Cu^{2+}	sulphate	SO_4^{2-}
magnesium	Mg^{2+}	carbonate	CO_3^{2-}
zinc	Zn^{2+}		
lead	Pb^{2+}		
iron(II)	Fe^{2+}		
iron(III)	Fe^{3+}		
aluminium	Al^{3+}		

Hazards

Harmful
These substances are similar to toxic substances but less dangerous.

Corrosive
These substances attack and destroy living tissues, including eyes and skin.

Irritant
These substances are not corrosive but can cause reddening or blistering of the skin.

Oxidizing
These substances provide oxygen which allows other materials to burn freely.

Highly flammable
These substances easily catch fire.

Toxic
These substances can cause death. They may produce their effects when swallowed or breathed in or absorbed through the skin.

Cleaning

Objectives

This spread should help you to

- describe what a detergent is
- describe how they work
- know the difference between detergent and soap

Detergents

The accidental release of large amounts of oil always gets reported. This is because of the harm it does to the environment and living things.

Detergents can help clear up disasters like this.

Detergents

Cleaning up an oil spill is similar to washing up after cooking a fried meal. Lots of 'washing-up' liquid is needed. These are usually made from detergents. **Detergents** are substances that help water to spread and clean. They are sometimes called **'wetting' agents**.

Oils, fats, and greases do not mix with water. They form 'blobs' and collect together. Water cannot get inside the blobs. A detergent molecule has a 'head' and a 'long tail'. The head is 'water-loving'. The long tail is a long-chain hydrocarbon. It is 'water-hating'. It is not attracted to water but to other hydrocarbon-containing molecules such as oil, fat, or grease.

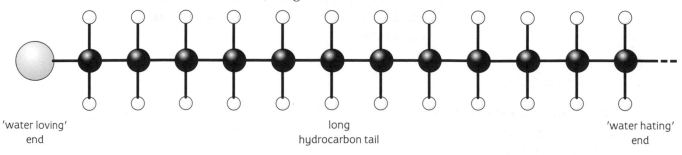

'water loving' end   long hydrocarbon tail   'water hating' end

A detergent molecule.

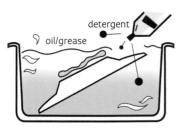
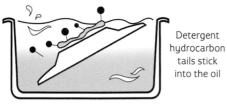

Detergent hydrocarbon tails stick into the oil

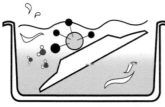

Water molecules attract the water-loving end and pull the oil and detergent into the water

How a detergent works.

Left: Not all skin cleansers are soaps or detergents.
Right: Shampoos must keep hair shiny as well as clean.

The tail dissolves in the oil, fat, or grease. The water-loving end sticks out. This end is attracted by the water and the pull of the water pulls the oil or fat off the surface of the plate.

When the oil, fat, or grease has been pulled right off, more detergent tails can dissolve in it. It then gets surrounded by more water molecules.

Detergents may help this animal survive.

Soaps

Soaps are made from animal fats and plant oils. They work in the same way as detergents.

Some water has a lot of calcium ions in it. This is called **'hard' water**. Water with only small amounts of calcium ions in it is called **'soft' water**. When soap is used in hard water a scum forms. To prevent this, soapless detergents are used. The detergents produced from crude oil hydrocarbons are soapless. These can be used in hard or soft water areas. No scum forms.

Cleaning gels or creams have been known since Roman times. Romans melted beeswax with olive oil. They mixed in rosewater and whisked it into an emulsion. An oil-in-water emulsion is water with oil droplets spread out in it. Many modern cleansing creams and sauces such as salad creams are **emulsions**.

Questions

1 What is a detergent and what is soap?
2 What do detergents do?
3 Describe how detergents work on grease.

4 What metal ion causes water to be 'hard' and what does 'hard' mean?

Answers

Answers are generally for numerical questions though pointers are given to some non-numerical questions. The answers are arranged in four sections:

answers to end of spread questions

answers end of module questions

answers to exam style questions

answers to multi-choice questions

Answers to end of spread questions

5.01

3

Robert Boyle (1627-1691)	1661	Idea of element as building blocks
John Dalton (1766-1844)	1808	Idea of the atom in all element and atomic weight
John Newlands (1837-1898)	1863	Newlands' law of octets
Dimitri Mendeleev	1869	First Periodic Table

5.04

2 Group 1 metals react to release hydrogen and leave an alkali solution.

3 The melting and boiling points decrease as you go down the group

5.06

3 Zinc displaces the silver to form silver metal and zinc nitrate. Zinc is the most reactive.

5.13

3 NaOH (aq) + HCl (aq) → NaCl (aq) + H_2O(l)

5.15

3

Zinc metal	+	Hydrochloric Acid	→	zinc chloride	+	hydrogen gas	+	energy change
Zn(s)	+	2HCl(aq)	→	$ZnCl_2$	+	H_2(g)		

4

Copper oxide	+	Sulphuric acid	→	Copper sulphate	+	Water	+	energy change
CuO(s)	+	H_2SO_4	→	$CuSO_4$(aq)	+	H_2O		

6.05

2 Liquid with higher boiling points condense at different times to ones with lower boiling points.

6.08

2 Metals, glass, paper, and textiles can be recycled

3 Biodegradable means the material can be broken down by biological action of bacteria (microrganisms).

4 Waste can be disposed of by landfill, recycling, or burning.

6.15

1 If a solid cools quickly the crystals will be small.

2 When magma cools quickly it will form obsidan or basalt

4 Large crystals form if a molten rock cools very slowly.

6.16

1 An igneous rock can be basalt, granite, or pumice.

2 Igneous means formed from molten rock. The molten rock comes from the Earth's centre and cools on the surface.

6.17

1 A sedimentary rock is chalk, limestone, or millstone grit.

6.18

1 A metamorphic rock is slate, schist, marble or

3 The starting material for marble is limestone.

7.01

1 To cause a reaction particles must collide.

2 The best states for a reaction to occur in are liquid or gas.

3 The particle in an atom involved in a chemical reaction is the electron.

4 Some reactions appear to lose mass because a product is released as a gas.

7.14

1 Nitric acid can be produced by oxidation of ammonia and then dissolving the nitrogen oxide in water.

2 When nitric acid and ammonia react, ammonium nitrate is formed.

Nitric Acid + Ammonium Hydroxide → Ammonium Nitrate + Water

$HNO_3(aq)$ + $NH_4(OH)(aq)$ → $NH_4NO_3(aq)$ + $H_2O(1)$

7.15

1 The number of particles represented are:

Li = 1 atom of lithium

P = 1 atom of phosphorus

Cu = 1 atom of copper

O_2 = 2 atom of oxygen = 1 molecule of oxygen

Cl_2 = 2 atom of chlorine = 1 molecule of chlorine

He = 1 atom of helium

3 the particle in an atom involved in a chemical reaction is the electron.

7.16

3 71%

4 11%

8.03

4

| Leucippus (480-420 BCE) | 500-350 BCE | Everything is made of |
| Democritus (460-370BCE) | | tiny bits called atoms |

| John Dalton (1766-1844) | 1808-1810 | Atoms are solid balls |
| Avogadro (1776-1856) | 1811 | Atoms join together to form molecules |

| JJ Thomson (1856-1940) | 1897 | Discovers electron e⁻ |

| Ernest Rutherford (1871-1937) | 1909 | Discovers proton p⁺ |

| James Chadwick | 1932 | Discovers Neutron n⁰ |

8.07

3 Shell 1 = 2 electrons when full

Shell 2 = 8 electrons when full

8.10

1 Common Salt

8.18

2

Metals	Semi-metal	Non-Metals
Sodium	Silicon	Phosphorus
Magnesium		Sulphur
Aluminium		Chlorine
		Argon

3 Silicon is a semi-metal – it has the highest melting point and is shiny and hard.

4 The melting and boiling points are different because of the packing of the atoms in the element.

8.20

2 As you go down the group the elements change from gas to liquid to solid, melting point and boiling point increases.

3 The reactivity decreases as you go down the group.

4 In group 1 and 2 the metal reactivity increases as you go down the group.

8.21

1 Noble gases are so called because they do not form bonds easily.

2 The outside electron shell of the noble gases are full.

3 It is not easy for the noble gases to form bonds.

8.24

2 Au   Hg   Al   Fe

3 Copper   Silicon   Oxygen   Calcium   Sodium

8.25

4 H_2O H = Hydrogen – 2 atoms   O = Oxygen – 1 atom

8.26

2 copper + oxygen → copper oxide

2Cu(s) + $O_2(g)$ → 2CuO(s)

3 iron + sulphur → iron sulphide

Fe(s) + S(s) → FeS(s)

A2

4 Calcium ions cause water to be hard. Hard water forms a scum with soap.

Answers to end of module questions

Module 5 (p44)

2 Mistakes are: alkaline earth (alkali) rubidium (potassium); 3 electrons (1); decrease (increase); high m.pts. (low); high densitives (low); oxygen (hydrogen); acid (alkali); gain (lose); negative (positive).

9 **a** iron(II) oxide; (hydrated) aluminium oxide; copper(II) sulphide

Module 7 (p126)

1 **a** 40 g, **b** 28 g, **c** 46 g, **d** 32 g, **e** 36.5 g, **f** 44 g,

4 **a iii** 69 cm^3, **a iv** 50 s, **b ii** B

13a 44/27%

b 180/40%

c 100/40%

20a $CH_4(g) + 2O_2(g) \rightarrow CO_2(g) + 2H_2O(g)$

b 16

c 16 × 55.6 = 890 kJ

29a 44, 27.3%

b 190, 40%

c 100, 12%

Module 8 (p184)

4 **b i** 88, **ii** 20, **iii** 108, **iv** 10.8

7 **a** A, B & E, **b** D, **c** C,

d A & B = magnesium atoms $^{24}_{12}Mg$ & $^{26}_{12}Mg$, C = magnesium ion Mg^{2+}

D = oxide ion O^{2-}

E = fluorine atom F

8 **a i** Al & N, **ii** O_2 & CH_4, **iii** Na^+ & I^-

b i sodium ion, **ii** iodide ion

c Sodium iodide NaI

11 **a i** NO_3^-, **ii** SO_4^{2-}, iii CO_3^{2-}, iv OH^-,

b i SrO, **ii** $SrCl_2$, **iii** $Cr(NO_3)_2$, **iv** $SrSO_4$

29 **b i** 2Na(s), 2NaCl(s), **ii** 2Mg(s), 2MgO(s), **iii** 2NaOH(aq), $2H_2O$(l), **iv** 2HCl(aq)

Answers to exam-style questions

2 **b** Group 7, **c** 7, **d i** 35 and 37, **ii** $^{35}_{17}Cl$ and $^{35}_{17}Cl$, **iii** isotopes

6 **a** copper metal

b water

c 8.0 g

d 6.4 g

e 1.6 g

f 1.8 g

8 **c** 1.8 g

11 a 1.8 g

16a 98 g

b 36.5 g

c 79 g

d 18 g

e 58.5 g

f 18 g

17a 25%

b 8%

c 57.5%

d 40%

24b i 28 g, **ii** 22 g

Answers to multi-choice questions

1	C	11	D
2	D	12	B
3	B	13	A & C
4	A	14	D
5	A	15	D
6	A	16	C
7	D	17	B
8	A	18	C
9	B	19	C
10	C	20	A

Index

Index